The Dandy really broke the mould in 1937. It was boisterous, anarchic and funny. It poked fun at authority. It had outlandish characters doing crazy things. It had animals who could walk and talk, and who were smarter than human beings. It was wonderful! The first issue of The Dandy sold 500,000 copies, but Britain's greatest comic would go on to sell more than 2 million copies a week in the swinging Sixties! In this book, we take a nostalgic look back at some of the highlights from the history of The Dandy. Find a comfy chair, make yourself comfortable, and we'll begin...

IN THE BEGINNING...

In the Thirties, D.C. Thomson was well-known as the publisher of the Big Five boys' adventure papers: Rover, Wizard, Hotspur, Skipper and Adventure. These were the Harry Potters of their day, devoured by millions of children every week.

These papers occasionally printed funny stories which proved popular with readers, so Albert Barnes, Chief Sub-Editor of Rover and Wizard, was asked to come up with a new comic which would be full of funny stories. That comic was The Dandy, and its first issue went on sale, complete with free "Express Whistler", in December 1937.

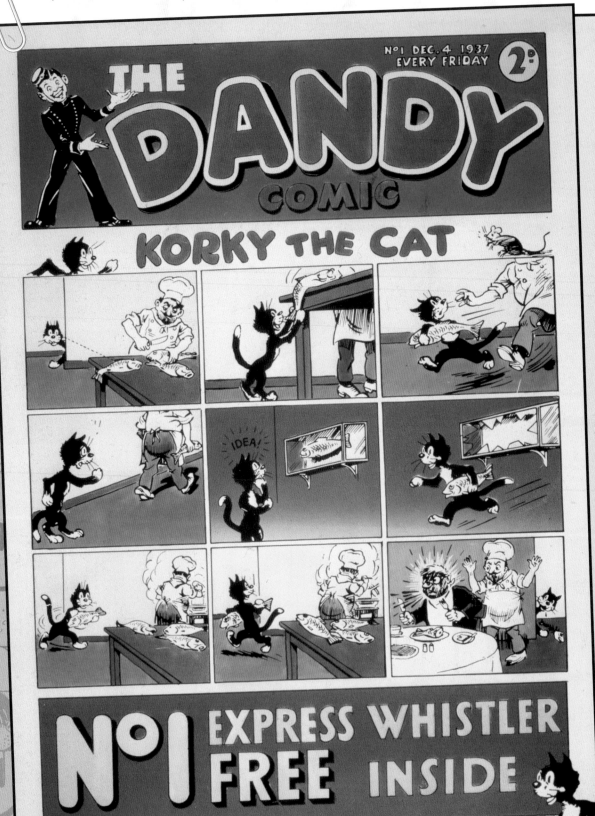

Korky the Cat would be the cover star of The Dandy for an amazing 47 years!

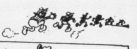

The new comic assembled a motley crew of outlandish characters, some of whom would go on to become household names.

The Dandy used a series of gifts to lure magpie-eyed readers into trying the new comic.

While The Dandy's main focus was on being funny, it also carried enough thrilling adventure stories to keep its readers on edge until the next issue came out. These adventures usually featured heroic underdogs fighting the good fight against villainy and overwhelming odds.

The Story of a Boy Sent to Fight a Tyrant King.

The shining sword of the shining sun
In the hands of a boy—the Fair-Haired One—
Shall bring death to the tyrant, so, Tyrant, beware
Of the sword of the sun and the son who is fair!

OMAR, The Wise Man.

THE MAGIC SWORD

KELMAN, The Fair-Haired Boy.

JASK, The Tyrant King.

The Thrilling Jungle Life of a Baby Elephant.

WEE TUSKY

The Great Story of a Boy and a Young Stag.

RED HOOF

The Thrilling Picture Story of Three Air Castaways.

LOST ON THE MOUNTAIN OF FEAR

A KORKER OF A COVER STAR!

Korky the Cat's mischievous antics captivated generations of readers. His early appearances were silent, but he soon developed a speaking voice which made him even more popular.

James Crichton's lovely, colourful artwork gave early issues of The Dandy a real wow factor!

INSIDE TODAY — DANNY LONGLEGS — The 10-Foot Schoolboy

No. 287 — MAR. 3rd, 1945

KORKY MADE A PAIR OF WINGS,
BUT KORKY COULDN'T FLY!
YET HOME-MADE WINGS ARE HANDY THINGS,
TO GET SOME FISH TO FRY!

CURIOSITY KILLED THE KATE!

A nosey girl who couldn't resist peering through other people's keyholes, Kate never learnt her lesson, despite getting her comeuppance every week!

In time, Kate developed a fondness for anything keyhole-shaped, but in these early strips it is her nosey parker nature which gets her into trouble.

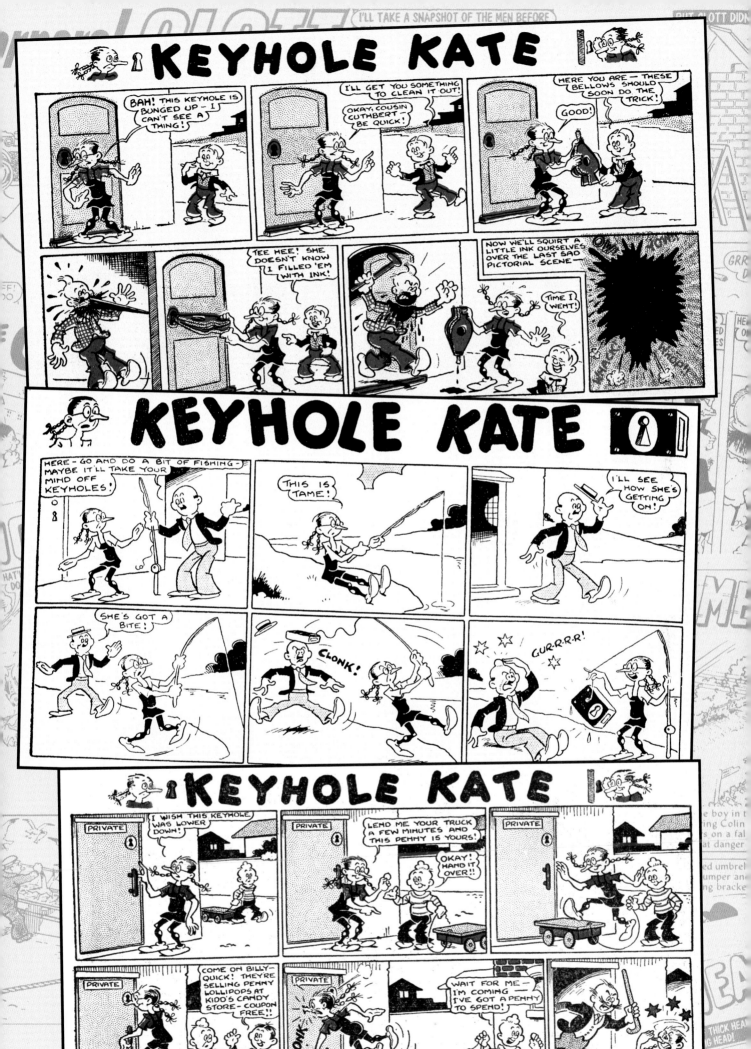

THE PRIMATE MOTIVE!

Bongo and Pongo are entrepreneurs - spivs with an eye on the main chance to make a few bucks. This lively comic strip had a huge cast of jungle characters whose joyous adventures really finished early numbers of The Dandy on a high note!

The animals are feeling ill, but they'll just have to lump it— Hippo's keeping them all awake with blasts from his huge trumpet.

BAMBOO TOWN

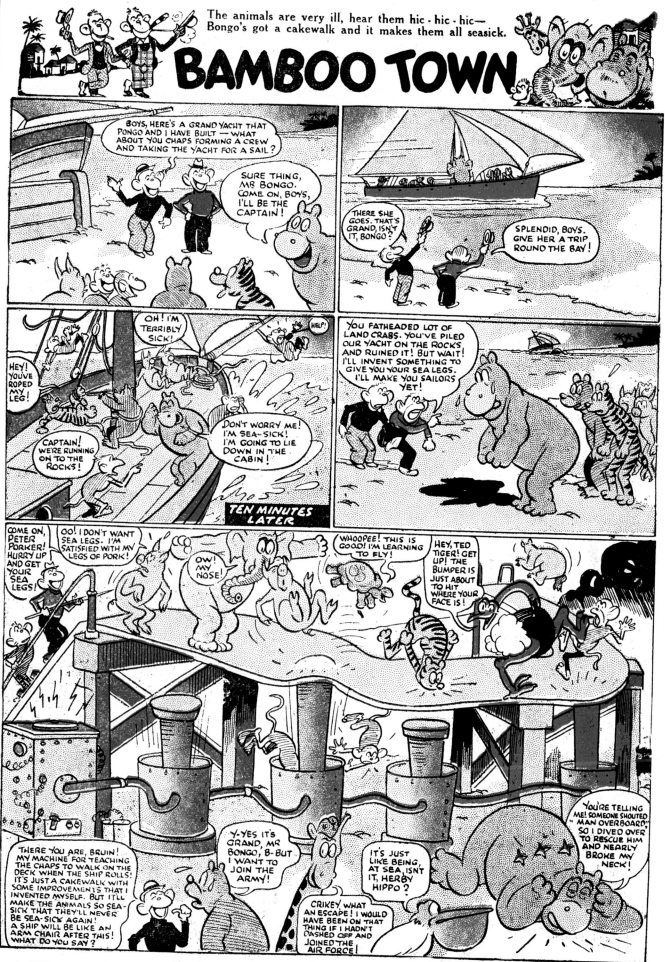

READY, FREDDIE, GO!

It's not easy being only a few millimetres tall, but Freddie the Fearless Fly makes up for it with enthusiasm and courage. Freddie's perilous insect life has plenty of ups and downs, but Freddie always buzzes back smiling!

DON'T SCOFF AT HORACE!

Horace only ever has one thing on his mind – his stomach! We're well-used to people loving food today, just like Horace, but when rationing was in force, anyone trying to have more than their fair share was fair game – no matter how devious Horace's schemes were, he usually ended up with only his just desserts!

A TALE OF TWO NASTIES!

During the early years of World War Two, The Dandy did its best to support the war effort by lampooning the opposition in the surreal and hilarious exploits of Addie and Hermy, the Nasty Nazis.
As the war dragged on, enthusiasm for the war effort was replaced by grim determination, and maybe it no longer seemed right to laugh at the exploits of the Nazis. Addie and Hermy were sent to 'der comic stockade in der sky'.

ADDIE AND HERMY
THE NASTY NAZIS

ONE MAN AND HIS SUPERDOG

Although Korky the Cat and Desperate Dan are the most famous Dandy stories, Black Bob has perhaps the most devoted following.

Leading lives which are pretty exciting for a shepherd and his dog, Andrew Glenn and Black Bob deal with the ne'er-do-wells and miscreants who threaten the rural calm of their valley.

Black Bob appeared hot on the heels of the success of Lassie Come Home, the first movie starring another remarkably intelligent collie.

Jack Prout's beautiful artwork is technically superb and rich in detail.

Who could look at these pages and fail to be drawn in?

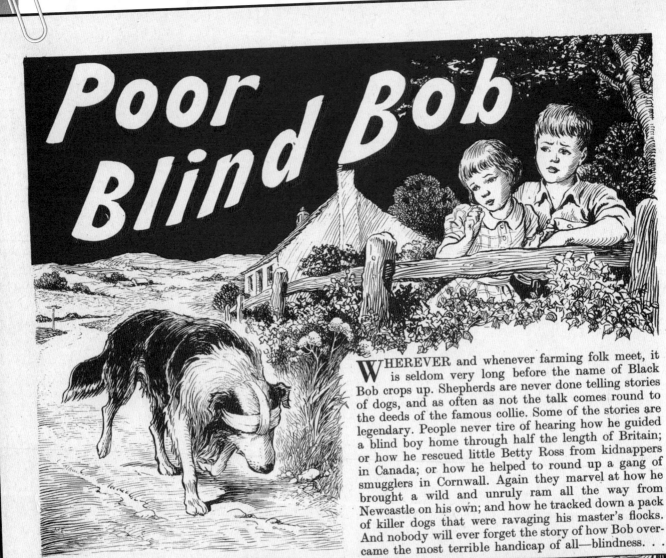

Poor Blind Bob

WHEREVER and whenever farming folk meet, it is seldom very long before the name of Black Bob crops up. Shepherds are never done telling stories of dogs, and as often as not the talk comes round to the deeds of the famous collie. Some of the stories are legendary. People never tire of hearing how he guided a blind boy home through half the length of Britain; or how he rescued little Betty Ross from kidnappers in Canada; or how he helped to round up a gang of smugglers in Cornwall. Again they marvel at how he brought a wild and unruly ram all the way from Newcastle on his own; and how he tracked down a pack of killer dogs that were ravaging his master's flocks. And nobody will ever forget the story of how Bob overcame the most terrible handicap of all—blindness. . .

It all began one autumn day when Bob was out working in the hills. He had run on ahead of his master looking for some stray sheep, when suddenly he heard screams. Black Bob rushed to the top of a rise. Below him was a caravan with flames belching from the doorway. Fleeing from the blaze was old Meg, the gipsy.

Meg had accidentally knocked over her paraffin stove. It flared up in a flash and the flames spread to the rug on which the stove had fallen. Black Bob came pelting up. He didn't hesitate. Bounding up the caravan steps, the brave collie seized a corner of the blazing rug and began to pull it outside, stove and all.

Black Bob's quick action undoubtedly saved the caravan. With the paraffin stove removed, the blaze was not nearly so fierce. When Andrew Glenn arrived he was able to get right inside the caravan with a bucket of water and put out what was left of the flames.

Old Meg was grateful. After the mess had been cleaned up, she made a cup of tea for the shepherd, and gave Black Bob some milk. "Now, I'll read your cup, Mr Glenn," she said when he was finished. But as soon as the old gipsy looked into the cup her face changed.

"Don't go any further than the hill today," she warned. "I foresee a terrible disaster." Andrew Glenn laughed. He didn't believe in fortune-telling. "Nonsense!" he grinned. "There's no danger on the hills, Meg." And in spite of old Meg's pleading, the big shepherd continued on his way with Black Bob.

An hour later, the weather suddenly changed. Great black clouds built up, and a terrible storm burst over the hills. "This must be the disaster Meg spoke about, Bob," grinned Glenn. "We're going to get soaked!" Even as he spoke lightning streaked into a tree a few feet away. Torn asunder, the tree toppled on Glenn.

For nearly five minutes Andrew Glenn lay there in the pouring rain, knocked senseless by the crashing tree. Then slowly his senses began to clear. With his head reeling, he looked around. What had happened to his beloved collie? Then he saw Bob, lying terribly still only a few feet away. Glenn's heart stood still.

Desperately the big shepherd struggled out from under the tree and hurried to the collie's side. "Bob! Bob!" he called anxiously. "Are you all right, lad?" There was no sign of any injury on the collie. Andrew Glenn felt Bob's heart. It was still beating. Then the limp muscles tensed, and Black Bob raised his head.

ANDREW GLENN sighed with relief when he saw Bob move. "You had me worried, lad," he said. "I thought you were badly hurt. Just a minute and I'll get you a drink." The shepherd hurried to the nearby stream. He knelt down and filled his cap with water.

Carrying his cap carefully, Glenn walked back to where Bob was lying. "Here you are, lad," he said. "Drink this." Bob did a surprising thing. He didn't seem to see the cap. He put his head down and sniffed around, as if he was expecting the drink to be on the ground!

Andrew Glenn's weather-beaten face turned pale. The cap fell from his fingers, and the water splashed on the ground and seeped away. Was it possible that Black Bob hadn't seen the water ? Had he been struck blind ? Andrew Glenn peered into the collie's eyes. Was this the disaster Gipsy Meg had foreseen ?

Picking Bob up, the shepherd rushed back down the hill. Farmer Grant drove them to see Mr McNab, the veterinary surgeon. McNab examined Bob's eyes. " Yes. Bob's blind," he said. " But don't despair. He has a good chance of recovery. I think you should take him to see Dr Wilson Baird, who lives in Manchester."

Mr McNab explained that Wilson Baird was an expert in animals' eyesight. The shepherd decided to take his advice. Next day he and Bob took a train to Manchester. Just as the train pulled in, one of the passengers, an old lady, cried out in dismay. "My money ! It's all gone ! Somebody has stolen it."

" This is serious," said Tom Burke, another of the passengers. " No one must leave until the police come." The sly-looking gent sitting next to the old lady looked furtive. He had stolen the money, and knew he would be in trouble if he was searched. Coolly he slid the stolen money under the coat on which Black Bob was sitting.

rporal CLOTT

I'LL TAKE A SNAPSHOT OF THE MEN BEFORE THEY LEAVE. COME ON, LADS—SCOWL! THIS IS A WAR PICTURE, SO YOU'VE GOT TO LOOK FIERCE!

BUT CLOTT DIDN'

I WAS TOO HIGH UP THERE! TRY DOWN HERE!

WE'RE GOING INTO BATTLE, CLOTT

Black Bob's eyes were bandaged, but he felt something moving under the coat. With an angry growl Bob turned, teeth flashing. Slick Mick let out a terrified yell. Bob's teeth had closed on his wrist. The money fell from his hand—just as a policeman arrived.

As the policeman led Mick away the old lady patted Black Bob gratefully. " Thank you very much, doggie," she said. " I hope your eyes will be all right soon." Andrew Glenn, meanwhile, was talking to Wilson Baird, who had come into the station to meet them.

As they drove away in the eye specialist's car, Wilson Baird questioned the shepherd about the accident that had robbed Bob of his sight. Then, at his clinic, he took Bob into the surgery. Andrew Glenn paced up and down outside the door. His beloved collie's future depended upon the skill of this one man.

After the examination Baird reached his decision. " I've good news for you, Mr Glenn," he said. " Y-you mean . . ." Glenn stammered in his excitement. " Yes," said Baird. " Bob will see again. But it will take time, and he must keep his eyes covered. I'd like you to leave him here so that I can watch his progress."

Andrew Glenn realised that this was best for Bob, and next day he set off for Selkirk. The big shepherd was sad at leaving the collie, but it was worse for poor blind Bob. He couldn't understand why his master had left him in this strange place. He lay with his head on his paws, pining and refusing to eat anything.

After two days Baird became worried. " I think he's lonely," he said. " We'll put him with the other dogs. That might help." It was feeding time. Baird put down some food for Bob. But because of his blindness, poor Bob trod on the plate, scattering the food. A hungry mongrel saw this and jumped in to try to get it.

B OB was shouldered aside. He staggered, heard the crunch of teeth on biscuits, and realised that this dog was stealing his food. With a snarl he flashed his teeth in the direction of the thief. It was a lucky shot. His teeth snapped on the greedy brute's ear.

The mongrel let out such a yowl that the attendant came rushing over to pull the mongrel away. For a moment Bob stood there uncertainly. Then the sound of a door creaking in the wind reached him. He knew that a noise like that usually meant an open door !

Bob's guess was right. The door of the pen had been left open. Guided by the creaking noise, the blind collie walked outside. None of the men saw him. He was free ! Now he could go and find his master. Bob walked on slowly, then—thump ! The poor blind collie had walked into the back of a lorry parked in the road.

The lorry smelt of milk. And milk to Black Bob meant a farm. Carefully, the blind collie clambered aboard. A few minutes later it was realised that Black Bob was missing. As Wilson Baird and his assistants searched the grounds, the lorry drove off—and for the first time since his master left him, Black Bob was happy.

The milkman had just finished his rounds and he was driving back to his dairy. Black Bob sat tight as the lorry twisted and turned through the back streets of Manchester. Bob had no idea where he was, but at least he was on his way. He wouldn't be able to rest until he had joined up with his beloved master again.

At last the lorry came to a stop. Bob got to his feet and stepped forward blindly. Thump ! Poor Bob had walked off the end of the lorry and hit the ground with an awful wallop. Dazed, he staggered up. He wasn't hurt, but it was a warning to the blind collie. He would have to be a great deal more careful in future.

THAT'S THE SPIRIT!

A story of British grit and bravery, Blitz Boy starred Quick Mick, a boy who had lost his memory during the blitz. After a series of gripping adventures, Mick was reunited with his parents in the end. They turned out to be rich department store owners, which was nice!

The adventures of a homeless boy in the desperate days of 1940.

BLITZ BOY

Little Tommy Jones's football became a casualty, burst by a falling stone. Tommy got his head cut as well, but he worried more about the ball.

Mick dragged him into the Underground station. There, an ambulance man dressed Tommy's injury, while he moaned about the useless football. "The boys'll scrag me for this," he said tearfully. Mick paid no attention at the time, for he was staring at a man in the air raid shelter—a man who seemed frightened. It was the same man Mick had seen receiving messages from a flower-seller.

DAY after day the Blitz continued. The full fury of German hate was turned on London during those terrible months of 1940. Fires blazed during the dark hours, yet the gallant firemen worked without rest to subdue the flames. Clearance squads made the streets safe, and London Town went to work again in the morning.

There were heroes by the hundred in those trying days, and one of them was undoubtedly Quick Mick. This was the boy who had lost his memory after being buried alive. During one raid a huge stone statue was blown up. The blast threw Mick against a little chap who had been hurrying by with a football under his arm.

When the "All Clear" sounded, Tommy ran off, but Mick trailed the mystery man. He was certain there was something queer about his connection with the flower-seller.

On the way, however, he ran into Tommy again, and Tommy had run into trouble. A gang of boys were chasing him, throwing sticks and stones at him for failing to take care of the gang's football.

Quick as thought, Mick pulled some marbles from a bag in his pocket. He threw them in front of Tommy's pursuers and saw the two leaders come a cropper. Tommy darted off—but Mick was to see him again, and very soon, too.

YES, SIREE! IT WAS A BRAINY IDEA OF MINE COMING TO THE RIVER TO GRAB OURSELVES A FREE FISH SUPPER THINK OF IT—SIZZLING HOT FRIED FISH, AND MAYBE SOME CHIPS THROWN IN! CAST AWAY, PAL!

OKAY! HERE GOES!

BIG HEAD and THICK HEAD

NOW LET US FOLLOW THE BACKWARD | A PARCEL OF FISH! WHAT'LL WE | PICTURE OF THICK HEAD

Blitz Boy takes the perilous cat-walk into danger — and out again!

Dodging those unfriendly chums of Tommy's, Mick took to the back alleys, and in one of them he saw Tommy again.

The little fellow had taken refuge in a back room of a ruined tenement, unaware that a fire was raging in the front. Now, as the flames ate through the walls, he was trapped. His yell for help made Mick look up.

Alarmed, Mick ran to the front of the building for help. Firemen were fighting another big fire here, and one of them promised to come in a moment.

Mick scurried back to see what he could do by himself. He placed a ladder across the alley from one ruin to the sill of the window where Tommy clung.

Steadily and surely, Quick Mick stepped out on the rungs, with never a thought about the risk of falling. He saw Tommy slump to the floor, overcome by smoke, and he made a reckless dive through the window.

Mick was really quick now. He had to be. As he slung the unconscious boy across his back, the flames were licking at the window frame. Out he stepped on the ladder again, while a group of people gazed up, dumb with horror.

It was touch and go. One split second lay between the two boys and certain death, for the ladder broke and fell as Mick stepped to safety on the broker wall.

Men of the rescue squad attended to Tommy while Mick stood by waiting till he saw Tommy recover.

Swiftly he sneaked a look at the boy's identity disc and walked away.

A free football for Tommy Jones — from young Santa Claus!

Before he returned to the basement of Perkins' Store, where he was now living, Mick spied on the flower-seller. The strange, grim-looking man came to her again and bought flowers.

But Quick Mick saw him toss the posy away! The stranger's interest was in the paper which had been wrapped round the stems! Clearly there was a message for him written there.

A minute or two later — Mick halted, baffled. The strange man had vanished in a maze of bombed houses.

And while he searched, near a timber yard, he suddenly heard the coughing stutter of a dying aeroplane engine. It was a Nazi bomber!

Mick took a dive, hugging the ground as the plane droned low overhead. It was going to crash, but before it did the crew jettisoned its incendiary bombs—and they fell into a woodyard.

Mick well knew how tremendous would be the blaze that might start up here. Running hard, he climbed a stack of planks, seized one, and used it to knock the burning bombs off the stacks.

Mick stifled the fire-bombs with sand. Someone called out the Fire Brigade, and the firemen, dirty, weary and hungry though they were, arrived and plunged into action within minutes.

Very little of the timber was lost, thanks to Quick Mick's heroic work. But the boy raced off when the fires were conquered. He had one more job to do.

Using the entrance known to himself alone, Mick returned to the unharmed basement of Perkins' Store, the place that was now his home. And in the Sports Department he chose a football from a pile.

Tommy Jones was asleep when his quiet visitor arrived at the address engraved on Tommy's identity disc. But he would be a happy lad when he woke up, and he wouldn't be scragged by the gang on the morrow!

Next week — Quick Mick's tank charge — in a baby's pram!

SUPER, SMASHING, GREAT!

The Smasher was The Dandy's answer to Dennis the Menace. Like Dennis, Smasher was out to cause as much mayhem as he could get away with, a calculation he almost always got wrong!

I'LL TAKE A SNAPSHOT OF THE MEN BEFORE THEY LEAVE. COME ON, LADS—SCOWL! THIS IS A WAR PICTURE, SO YOU'VE GOT TO LOOK FIERCE!

I WAS TOO HIGH UP THERE! TRY DOWN HERE!

THE SMASHER

LOOK AT THOSE MUGS! FANCY DIGGING HOLES ON SUCH A HOT DAY!

SUCCESS! WE'VE DUG UP A GOLD POT! YIPPEE!

GOLLY! THEY'VE FOUND GOLD! THEY'RE NOT SO DAFT AFTER ALL!

I'M HOPING TO STRIKE IT RICH HERE! THIS IS WHERE A BANK USED TO BE IN OLDEN TIMES!

I'VE STRUCK SOMETHING SOLID! IS IT SILVER OR GOLD?

WOW! IT'S A WATER MAIN!

LATER

HULLO! A MECHANICAL DIGGER—THAT'LL MAKE HOLE DIGGING EASIER!

HO-HO! THIS IS GREAT FUN! PITY I'VE FOUND NOTHING BUT EMPTY HOLES SO FAR!

WOW! NOW ONE OF THE HOLES IS FULL!

OOPS!

HO-HO! NOW THEY'LL HAVE TO EXCAVATE THE EXCAVATOR!

LATER

GOSH! WHAT A STROKE OF LUCK—A SHILLING! NOW I CAN HAVE A SUPER FEED AT TONI'S!

BOY! THAT WAS SMASHIN'!

HERE EES DA BILL.

BILL 1/-

WOW! THERE'S A HOLE IN MY POCKET AND I'VE LOST MY MONEY!

I'VE HEARD-A THESE-A TALES BEFORE!

TONI'S CAFE

COME-A BACK HERE!

NO FEAR!

NOW I'M REALLY IN A HOLE—BUT AREN'T I GLAD!

WHERE-A IS HE?

BOOM-BANG-A-BANG!

Bing Bang Benny was notable for two reasons. The first is that it was drawn by the legendary Ken Reid, who also drew Jonah. The second is that it features the best explosions ever drawn in a comic strip!

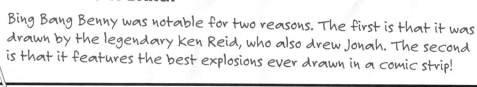

BING-BANG BENNY

WHAT'S THE IDEA, BENNY?

THE FORT'S SHORT OF WATER ~~

~AND THERE'S A LAKE ON THE OTHER SIDE OF THEM THAR HILLS, BUT THE INJUNS WON'T LET US GET TO IT ~

WARNING INDIAN TERRITORY

~SO I'M GONNA HOP OVER THAT INJUN TERRITORY ON MY ROCKET-PROPELLED BARRELS AND GET THEM FILLED. STAND CLEAR!

FIZZ

HO-HO! I'LL BE AT THAT LAKE AND BACK BEFORE THEM THAR INJUNS CAN BLINK AN EYELID.

WHOOSH

BANG

SUFFERIN' SNAKES! I'M OVERSHOOTING THE LAKE—AND I'M HEADIN' STRAIGHT FOR THE INJUN ENCAMPMENT.

ZOOM

JEEPERS! I'VE KNOCKED BIG CHIEF RUNNIN' WATER FLAT.

GASP!

THUD

SORRY, CHIEF, BUT I GOTTA TAKE YOU BACK TO THE FORT.

WHOOSH

WAH! UGH!

BANG

Next day~ UGH! THIS MESSAGE FROM PALE-FACE BING-BANG! HIM SAY WE GET UM BIG CHIEF BACK FOR 500 GALLONS OF WATER!

And so~ QUICK! YOU BRING MORE WATER FOR FORT! BIG CHIEF WANT TO GO HOME!

HEH-HEH! NO WATER SHORTAGE NOW!

BING-BANG-BENNY

HOWDY, FOLKS! I'M GONNA INVENT A NEW, POWERFUL EXPLOSIVE~

BUT THE SHERIFF SENT ME OUT HERE SO'S I WON'T BLOW THE WHOLE FORT SKY-HIGH.

CHEMISTRY SET

HERE'S A GOOD SPOT TO WORK.

HEE-HEE! WE STEAL UM NUTS FROM FORT. NOW WE HAVE HEAP GOOD TUCK-IN!

UM YUM!

CHESTNUTS

I GO COLLECT MORE WOOD FOR FIRE! DON'T FORGET TO PRICK UM NUTS — OR THEY GO POP.

DA-OK!

BUT SUDDENLY~

DEAR-UM-ME! WE FORGET TO PINCH UM SALT TO SPRINKLE ON NUTS!

(POP)

FIZZ

OH, BOY! THIS WHIZZ-WHAM MIXTURE'S GONNA BE MIGHTY POWERFUL!

BLOOP! SIZZLE

AH! PALEFACE BOY—HIM COOKUM MEAL! PLENTY SEASONING! ME CREEP ROUND ROCKS AND PINCH UM SALT!

AND SO~

GOT UM!

BACK AT THE NUT-ROASTING FIRE~

HEE-HEE! ~ ME PINCH UM SALT FROM PALEFACE BOY! VERY UM TASTY, VERY UM~

SHAKE

BOOM

SUFFERIN' SNAKES! WHAT WAS THAT?

HO-HO! THE SHERIFF SURE WILL BE PLEASED TO SEE THESE TWO GUYS.

GASP!

GOOD WORK, BENNY! WE'LL KEEP 'EM AS HOSTAGES.

SON OF NIT-WIT! YOU FORGET TO PRICK UM NUTS!

MUDDLE OF HONOUR!

A child (and not a clever child at that!) trapped in soldier's body, Clott is well-meaning but ill-starred, leading to endless frustration for his superior officer, Colonel Grumbly.

National Service was still compulsory until 1963, meaning every Dandy reader could expect to find themselves in Clott's army boots – or, if they were better-off, Colonel Grumbly's!

Corporal CLOTT

I'LL TAKE A SNAPSHOT O[F] THEY LEAVE. COME ON, [IT] IS A WAR PICTURE, SO...

I'LL CLIMB UP THIS TREE AND SEE IF I CAN SPOT ANYONE ARRIVING.

EEK! IT'S COLLAPSING!

I'D BETTER CLEAR OFF! THEY'RE LOOKING TOO FIERCE NOW FOR MY LIKING!

HERE, PRIVATE POTTS, YOU'D BETTER TAKE THIS OTHER CAMERA! CLOTT IS OBVIOUSLY GOING TO BE USELESS.

LATER, NEAR THE FRONT LINE

THIS IS WHERE THE BATTLE'S SUPPOSED TO BE, BUT I CAN'T SEE A SOUL! MAYBE I'VE COME TOO EARLY!

FURTHER ON—

HELLO, SIR! IS THIS YOUR HEADQUARTERS? I'LL COME IN AND TAKE A SNAP OF YOU.

IT'S DARK IN HERE, SO I'LL HAVE TO USE FLASH POWDER. SCOWL, PLEASE!

GOSH! THE FLASH POWDER HAS SET THE TENT ALIGHT!

EEEK!

SUDDENLY CLOTT TRIPS

OOOPS!

GIVE ME MY CAMERA, YOU CHEEKY MONKEY!

BACK AT CAMP PRIVATE POTTS REPORTS—

SORRY, SIR, BUT I COULDN'T GET ANY WAR PICTURES!

I KNOW! CLOTT BUNGLED EVERYTHING. THE GENERAL WILL BE FURIOUS. WE'VE NO PICTURES TO SHOW HIM!

SUDDENLY—

HERE I AM—I'LL HAVE THE PICTURES READY IN TEN MINUTES!

WELL, SIRS[,] DO YOU T[HINK] THAT? SM[ILE,] EH?

CORPORAL CLOTT

THE RED PERIL!

The Crimson Ball was the creation of The Master, who had enslaved Peter Jones to lead him to every military airbase in the country, where the Ball would destroy the aircraft. Unfortunately, how Peter knew where the airbases were (and the Master didn't) is not explained!

The Crimson Ball creeps from the sea to fight against its Master!

THE CRIMSON BALL

THE Crimson Ball was at the bottom of the sea. It was riddled with holes from a fighter plane's guns and was rapidly filling with water. Peter Jones, the schoolboy trapped inside, was fighting for his life.

With the end of a mop gripped in his teeth, the boy was fishing under the water, trying to click the switch which controlled the manacles that held him.

Click! He had done it!

Peter was released He got a hammer from a toolbox.

With pounding blows, he destroyed the iron cuffs so that he wouldn't be tricked into being a prisoner again.

Now, seated at the controls, Peter ducked under the water to find the switches that would set the Ball in motion.

Using the senseless cop as a shield, he fished a revolver from inside his tunic and shot at two other policemen who came towards him. He dragged his victim into an abandoned cottage.

Meanwhile, on land, the mystery Master of the Crimson Ball had suddenly attacked the policeman nearest to him.

The cops were forced to seek cover when the Master fired from a window.

Peter had now succeeded in starting the motors of the Crimson Ball. It rolled over the sea-bed till it gained the sandy beach at the foot of the cliffs.

rporal CLOTT

I'LL TAKE A SNAPSHOT OF THE MEN BEFORE THEY LEAVE. COME ON, LADS—SCOWL! THIS IS A WAR PICTURE, SO YOU'VE GOT TO LOOK FIERCE!

I WAS TOO HIGH UP THERE! TRY DOWN

BUT CLOTT DIDN'

The Master beats the cops — But can he beat the Crimson Ball?

On the level again, the boy stared into the TV scanner in the Crimson Ball until he sighted the Master. There he was, firing from the cottage window. Peter steered for the cottage.

Now, with sea-water gurgling out of the shellholes at every movement, the Crimson Ball rolled up the narrow footpath that led to the cliff-top. Faintly, Peter could hear the reports of revolver shots.

The two cops sheltering from the bullets seized on the chance of cover given by the Crimson Ball. They followed behind it. But, just then, a man with his hands up staggered from the cottage.

The policemen rushed to grab him—then realised that this was their own mate stripped of his tunic. "He went out the back window," said the dazed policeman.

Sure enough, the masked man had sneaked outside and worked his way round till he was behind the Crimson Ball. Now he was running desperately —trying to take Peter by surprise.

Even as the Master took off in a mighty leap, striving to reach the open hatch, Peter heard the noise of thudding feet. Just in time, he dropped inside the Ball and slammed the hatch.

Foiled, the Master drew his gun once more to shoot at the policemen. But the Crimson Ball came rolling at him and revolver shots couldn't penetrate it. With a gasp of dismay, the Master turned and ran—with the Crimson Ball pounding after him!

Next week — The chase that ended in disaster for Peter Jones!

BUT ARE TWO HEADS BETTER THAN ONE?

Another classic strip by Ken Reid, Big Head and Thick Head was the story of two schoolboys (one clever and one stupid) whose escapades proved that one and one actually equals DUMB!

BIG HEAD AND THICK HEAD

IT'S PLAYTIME AT SCHOOL, AND THICK HEAD HAS SNEAKED OUT TO THE BIKE SHED—

HEE-HEE-HEE! I'M IN A PRACTICAL JOKING MOOD TODAY! WHEN THE TWO STUPID NITS WHO OWN THESE BIKES TRY TO RIDE THEM OFF AT LUNCH-TIME, THEY'LL GET THE SHOCK OF THEIR LIVES!

JUST YOU WATCH WHAT HAPPENS!

LUNCH TIME—AND FOR ONCE THICK HEAD'S PEA-SIZED BRAIN ACHIEVES THE DESIRED RESULTS! THE CYCLISTS LEAP ASTRIDE THEIR MACHINES AND THE TWO STUPID NITS GET THE SHOCK OF THEIR LIVES—

AR-R-R-RGH-H! SOME BIG CLOT HAS TIED OUR BLITHERING BIKES TOGETHER!

OH, NO!

LATER—WHILE BIG HEAD IS AWAY LOOKING FOR THE CLOT WHO TIED THE BIKES TOGETHER—

OKAY!— SO I BOOBED WITH THAT PRACTICAL JOKE. BUT I AIN'T COMPLETELY DUMB, AND I'LL PROVE IT! WATCH ME CATCH FATTY TUBBS OUT WITH THIS APPLE. HE'LL BE COMING THIS WAY IN A MINUTE.

ORCHARD KEEP OUT

HERE HE COMES! NOW WATCH! IT'S A RUBBER SQUIRTER-APPLE, AND WHEN I SQUEEZE THIS BULB—

OH, BOY! AN APPLE— ERK! GLUB!

HEE-HEE!

HO-HO-HO! IT WORKED! I'VE PULLED OFF A JOKE WITHOUT IT BACKFIRING ON ME! HA-HA! POOR OLD TUBBY!

ARF-ARF!

ORCHARD KEEP OUT

HA-HA-H-AGH-H! NO! BLIMEY! WHAT'S UP? OUCH!

YOU PINCHED THAT FROM MY ORCHARD, DIDN'T YOU? DON'T ARGUE! TAKE THAT!

BIFF BAM

BACK IN SCHOOL, JUST BEFORE THE AFTERNOON SESSION—

HO-HO! SO YOU BOOBED, EH, THICK HEAD? RIGHT! NOW I'LL SHOW YOU THE INGENIOUS WAY OF PRACTICAL JOKING ON TEACHER! SEE! I'M SAWING HALFWAY THROUGH A LEG OF HIS STOOL—AND YOU HIDE HIS CANE, JUST TO BE ON THE SAFE SIDE.

OKAY!

AFTERNOON SESSION BEGINS—

RIGHT! WE'LL START WITH HIST—! ER-R-RK! WHERE'S ME CANE?

COR! NOW WE'RE FOR IT!

PSSST! DON'T WORRY, BASHER! WE'VE HIDDEN HIS CANE!

CRACK

AFTER ONE FRUITLESS SEARCH—

GRR! MY CANE'S GONE! BUT HERE'S A HANDY SUBSTITUTE! THE WHOLE CLASS PREPARE FOR WALLOPING!

WOW! THE LEG OF HIS STOOL!

AND SO—

SNARL! I'LL MAKE SURE I PUNISH THE CULPRIT! BEND DOWN, THE LOT OF YOU.

WHACK
AGH!
WHAM
SWIPE
EEK!
THWACK
OUCH!
SWISH
OO-YAH!

AFTER SCHOOL—

AH! THERE YOU ARE, BIG HEAD! I'D LIKE A WORD WITH YOU, PAL! YOU MADE A RIGHT HASH OF THAT PRACTICAL JOKE, DIDN'T YOU?

W-WELL—ER—HEE-HEE! IT COULD HAVE GONE OFF BETTER!

OF COURSE, IT AIN'T ENTIRELY YOUR FAULT! UNLIKE YOUR CLOT OF A PAL, YOU LOOK BRAINY! PEOPLE EXPECT BRAINY THINGS OF YOU—BUT NOTHING YOU DO COMES OFF! YES, MATE, IT'S THAT WELL-GROOMED, BRAINY LOOK THAT GETS YOU INTO TROUBLE. BUT I THINK I CAN ALTER THAT, MATE!

R-REALLY! H-H-HOW?

SNARL!— LIKE THIS! AND THIS! AND THIS! AND THIS! AND THIS!

SWIPE
KRAK
SQUELCH
KRUNCH
AGH-H-H-H! ME TEEPH— ME DOSE!
WHOOSH

AFTER THE ALTERATION

BLAH-H! BURBLE! GIBBER! SLOBBER! GABBLE!

YOU SEE PAL, IT DOESN'T PAY TO LOOK BRAINY! BUT NEVER MIND! NOW THAT YOU LOOK A PRIZE NIT LIKE ME, MAYBE WE'LL STAY OUT OF TROUBLE, EH?

DICK-IN-THE-MUD!

Dick couldn't keep himself clean, much to the frustration of his prim and proper parents. Another lovely piece of work by Eric Roberts, Dick's adventures in untidiness continued for eighteen years.

DIRTY DICK

MY WORD, DICK, YOU ARE CLEAN AND TIDY! MUM WILL BE PLEASED WHEN SHE BRINGS IN THE BREAKFAST!

GOOD MORNING DAD!

JUST LOOK IN THE HALL AND SEE IF THE PAPER'S COME YET, DICK!

NOT YET, DAD! DON'T WORRY, I'LL NIP DOWN TO THE GATE AND SEE IF THE BOY'S IN SIGHT!

OWCH! CLUMSY!

OOPS! SORRY, MR. POSTMAN!

CRASH!

ER, I WAS LOOKING FOR THE PAPER BOY!

OH, WERE YOU? WELL, YOU'VE MISSED HIM— HE PASSED ME UP THE ROAD!

GOSH! HE'S FORGOTTEN US! I'LL NIP OVER THE WALL AND OVERTAKE HIM!

WHOOPS! TRUST JIMMY JONES TO LEAVE HIS SKATES OUT ALL NIGHT!

WHIZZ!

HOI! WHAT ABOUT MY DAD'S PAPER?

NUTS TO YOU, DIRTY DICK, AND I DIDN'T KNOW YOUR FATHER COULD READ!

GRR! I'LL BELT YOU FOR THAT!

OH YEAH?

OO! OW! UGH! MY DAD'LL REPORT YOU TO OLD NATTER THE NEWSAGENT FOR THAT!

SO WHAT...?

.... I DON'T WORK FOR HIM— I DELIVER PAPERS FOR OLD MAGGS!

OO-ER! THE WRONG PAPER BOY!

AH, THERE'S DICK! OKAY, SON, THE PAPER CAME JUST AFTER YOU WENT. COME ON IN AND LET YOUR MUM SEE HOW NICE AND CLEAN YOU ARE......

EEEK!

GOOD MORNING, MUM!

OH NO, I DON'T BELIEVE IT! HE'S ONLY BEEN OUT FOR FIVE MINUTES!

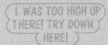

YOU CAN'T BEAT A BIT OF BULLY!

While Albert Barnes insisted that the only violence in The Dandy was of the cartoon sort, one strip in particular came painfully close to reality. Bully Beef and Chips had a brutally simple storyline: Bully Beef beats Chips up... for absolutely no reason.

Luckily, the Rules of Comic Justice* decreed that Beefy would be the one who ended up seeing stars. However, anyone who has been bullied will recognise the random mindlessness of Bully's behaviour.

*Rules of Comic Justice #1: In any violent comic encounter, the Original Assailant shall be defeated and humiliated by his Victim, no matter how unlikely that seems at the beginning of the Assault.

BULLY BEEF AND CHIPS

HO-HO! LOOK AT ME! I'M A BIKE-BUSTER! RIDE 'IM, COWBOY!

BUMP!

RATTLE!

SO BULLY BEEF'S BUST YOUR BIKE. WHAT ARE YOU GOING TO DO, CHIPS?

FIX THE BIKE—AND BULLY BEEF AT THE SAME TIME!

LATER. CHIPS HAS REPAIRED THE BIKE. GOOD! I'LL NAB IT AND HAVE MORE FUN.

VAMOOSE, SMALL TIMER! I'M GOING FOR A RIDE ON YOUR IRON STEED!

OOYAH!

BUT—

EEEK! THE HANDLE-BARS HAVE COME OFF!

CRUMBS! I'VE COLLIDED WITH TEACHER AND KNOCKED HIM INTO THE CANAL.

GLUG!

BAM!

A FEW SECONDS LATER CHIPS ARRIVES—

HO-HO! BULLY BEEF HAS GONE FOR A SWIM, I THINK!

YOU, BOY! YOU'RE A RECKLESS DRIVER! TAKE A HUNDRED LINES!

HO-HO! CHIPS GOT THE BLAME! HA-HA-HA!

AND YOU, BOY, TAKE A HUNDRED LINES FOR LAUGHING. THIS IS NO JOKE!

OOER!

LATER

AH! CHIPS IS DOING HIS LINES. WELL, THEY'LL BE MINE SHORTLY...

THANKS, KID—THIS IS A STICK-UP!

SNATCH

OUCH!

NOW WATCH THIS NEXT STICK-UP!

THE LINES HAVE STUCK TO THE LOLLIPOP! THANKS, CHIPS!

BULLY BEEF HANDS IN HIS LINES.

A BLANK SHEET OF PAPER?

IT'S THE CANE FOR YOU!

I WAS EXPECTING TROUBLE, SO I USED VANISHING INK!

OOER!

IT REAPPEARS WHEN YOU HEAT THE PAPER.

HERE ARE MY LINES, SIR!

WELL DONE, CHIPS!

AFTER SCHOOL

HIYA, BULLY BEEF. DO YOU WANT A RIDE ON MY BIKE—OR ARE YOU TOO SADDLE SORE, COWBOY?

GRR!

Printed and Published in Great Britain by D. C. THOMSON & Co., Ltd., 12 Fetter Lane, Fleet Street, London, E.C.4.
© D. C. THOMSON & Co., Ltd., 1966.

Football and adventure collide in this strip. Mysterious gangsters kidnap famous footballers with their amazing hovercar. Young Jinky Baker is a huge football fan – and he's out to stop the hovercar snatchers...

The strangest car-chase ever — It takes place on the SEA!

The HOVERCAR SNATCHERS

It was a half-holiday at Shottenham High School — and first out the gate was Jinky Baker!

Soon he was pedalling towards Sandley, the neighbouring town. No dinner today. Jinky's favourite team, Shottenham Rovers were training on the beach there—and he couldn't miss THAT!

But at Sandley, Jinky was stopped. Squads of policemen were guarding the beach. One of them was his father, Detective Constable Jack Baker. "We're making sure the Hovercar Snatchers don't get Jim Colley, the Rovers' internationalist," he told Jinky. "They've tried once, and they may try again. Sorry, son, but I can't let you on the beach!"

NO ADMITTANCE

Glumly Jinky wandered off. The Hovercar Snatchers were crooks who, for some strange reason, were kidnapping international footballers. Jinky strolled on to a little pier. He could watch the Rovers from there. He could also see a landing craft approaching.

SPEEDBOAT TRIPS 5/-

Suddenly, down dropped the ramp on the landing craft—and a strange car without wheels shot over the surface of the water towards the beach. Jinky gasped. It was the Hovercar!

The footballers—and the police—were taken by surprise. Three toughs leapt from the Hovercar, firing blasts of knock-out gas from strange-shaped guns. Policemen and footballers alike slumped to the ground. Roughly one of the toughs grabbed Jim Colley and hauled him into the Hovercar. The Snatchers had got the man they wanted.

Jinky whirled to the man working on his speedboat nearby. "Quick!" he gasped. "The Hovercar Snatchers have got Jim Colley! We've got to stop them." "Got Jim Colley, have they? Right, lad! Hop in!" snapped Mike Ranson, the boat-man.

"This boat's the fastest in these parts," boasted Mike. "We'll soon overhaul the Hovercar—even though it does ride above the surface of the water!"

The speedboat slowly drew level with the Hovercar.

"Now we've got 'em!" said Mike. He shot past the Hovercar and swung across its path. "Now they'll have to stop!"

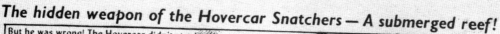

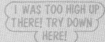

I WAS TOO HIGH UP THERE! TRY DOWN HERE!

The hidden weapon of the Hovercar Snatchers — A submerged reef!

But he was wrong! The Hovercar didn't stop! The shrill whine of its air jets increased, and the Hovercar leapt clean over the speedboat. "It's no good!" said Jinky. "We'll never stop them! Just stay behind them. We'll maybe find out where their hide-out is!"

Arnold Bate, the crooks' leader, snarled in anger as the speedboat fell back and began to follow them.

"We'll fix them!" he snapped, and altered course. The speed-boat followed on.

But suddenly, "Look out!" yelled Jinky. "Rocks!" Desperately Mike swung the steering wheel. But he was too late.

With a crash of splintering timbers the boat ran on to a submerged reef that ripped open her bows. The stern lifted from the waves, pitching Jinky and Mike into the sea. The Hovercar Snatchers had led them into a trap. Again Arnold Bate had triumphed.

Desperately Jinky and Mike battled through the surging waves towards the shore.

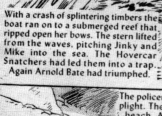

The policemen on shore had spotted their plight. They formed a life chain from the beach. A strong arm grabbed Jinky.

Seconds later Mike was helped ashore. It had been a near thing! Jinky had come very close to drowning—but he found that almost as bad a thing had happened to him! His autograph album was absolutely sodden!

Next week — How the Hovercar Snatchers were foiled — By a goal net that fell from the skies!

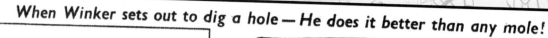

Thanks to Winker's wily ways — He's feeding now on luxuries!

BACK TO WORK, WATSON — AND THIS TIME I'LL MAKE SURE YOU DON'T ESCAPE!

GET BUSY! ROLL THE LAWN!

BAH! Another job! This time he was tied to his task.

PUFF! GASP!

While Ginger Jones steered the roller, Winker did the donkey work.

WHEW! THANKS FOR (PUFF!) TRYING TO HELP, BOUNCER! (GASP!)

GRR-R-R-R

HUH! The lawn sloped upwards! However, Bouncer lent a hand with his mouth!

SNAP!

But suddenly the strain went off—and so did the roller! Bouncer's sharp teeth had severed the rope!

GOSH! THAT WAS WELL AIMED!

CRASH!

Downhill rumbled the roller—and bulldozed its way through the school's back gate!

RUN FOR IT, BOYS!

COME BACK! COME BACK!

WHEW! GASP! I HAVEN'T GOT THE STRENGTH TO ESCAPE! GASP!!

Form Three downed tools and ran. But Winker could hardly crawl. That roller had fagged him out.

By good chance the Headmaster came into the garden. He took pity on Winker.

GOODNESS! SURELY MR. CREEP HAS BEEN MAKING WATSON DO ALL THE WORK HIMSELF! HE'S EXHAUSTED!

GASP!!

NOW I'VE ROUNDED ALL YOU BOYS UP, YOU CAN CARRY ON WITH THE GARDEN WORK!

HO-HO! THANKS TO THE HEAD, I'VE GOT OUT OF CREEPY'S CLUTCHES AFTER ALL!

HEAD

POP

BISCUITS

So Winker spent the afternoon in the Head's study, using the last of his strength, guzzling cakes and pop! What a wily wangler!

Next week — Piles of laughs when Winker tries to sell piles of books.

Winker WATSON

Winker Watson is on the loose — Putting piles of books to many a use.

GREYTOWERS SCHOOL library was in a mess — and Winker Watson, of Form Three, was in for a lot of work. Mr Creep, his Housemaster, gave him and his pal, Ginger, some book work. But the wily wangler soon turned despair into joy.

SILENCE

THOSE OLD BOOKS ARE CLUTTERING UP THE LIBRARY — GET RID OF THEM, YOU TWO BOYS!

WE'LL SELL THEM TO THE SECONDHAND BOOKSHOP!

PHEW! THEY'RE HEAVY. ISN'T THERE AN EASIER WAY OF BRINGING THEM OUT?

Winker had an easy way of getting the books outside.

YES — WE'LL JUST THROW THEM OUT OF THE WINDOW!

OW!

What a pity the easy way was hard on old Creepy! The falling books floored him as he passed by.

LET'S GO BEFORE OLD CREEPY RECOVERS!

Winker had an amazing school record — he had never once been caned. He beat it before his record could be broken!

SEE — WE DON'T NEED MONEY!

All that their entry cost was two minutes' work — erecting Winker's special book-ladders!

STOP, BERT — WE'LL HAVE A LOOK AT THE MATCH!

BUT WE'VE NO MONEY, WINKER!

RANGERS v TOWN

FOO

Lack of money wasn't going to stop Winker. He knew how to get in.

SO! I SUSPECT THAT'S WATSON'S IDEA!

It didn't take Creepy long to put two and two together!

OY!

But before he could climb the "ladder," a bobby spied him — and tried to book him!

HA-HA! THAT WAS A LUCKY ESCAPE FOR US!

Old Creepy showed him the cleanest pair of heels in town!

After the match, Winker and Ginger went off to sell the books.

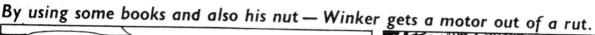

By using some books and also his nut — Winker gets a motor out of a rut.

I'LL GIVE YOU A PENNY EACH FOR 'EM!

OKAY!

YAH, I'M NOT SELLING MY HALF TO THAT OLD SKINFLINT!

BOOKS BOUGHT AND SOLD

But the price didn't suit Winker. He trundled the barrow off in search of a better bargain.

GOSH! THERE'S SOMEONE IN TROUBLE!

Winker went to investigate

The car's front wheel was stuck in a hole.

HOW?

MAYBE THESE BOOKS WILL HELP, MISTER.

THAT'S THE WAY, MISTER — YOUR CAR WILL BE CLEAR IN NO TIME!

One pile of books helped to make a jack. As the driver levered the wheel up an inch at a time, Winker slid books under the wheel.

The books gradually filled the hole, and the car was on an even keel again. Winker's scheme had paid off!

GOLLY, THANKS! NOW I DON'T NEED TO SELL THE BOOKS!

I'LL GET RID OF THEM ON THIS LORRY!

"Wealthy" Winker decided to give up the book business. He gave his books away.

TRANSPORT

But Creepy was awaiting Winker's return outside school. And Winker was still in his master's black books!

GOT YOU, WATSON — BEND OVER!

OLD CREEPY!

A BOOK, EH? THAT OLD TRICK ISN'T GOING TO FOOL ME!

Creepy investigated Winker's bulge—and found an anti-caning device! He threw the book on the ground.

VOL. II

It looked as if Winker's caning record would be broken.

HELP!! WHAT'S ALL THIS?

But no! A passing lorry rocked as it ran over the book. And a load of books toppled off it—on to Creepy! This was the lorry on which Winker had dumped the books! What luck!

I GUESS I WIN!

GASP!

Winker grinned as he ran off. His record was intact and he was still tops at wangling—he had a ten bob note to prove it!

Next Tuesday — Creepy is dogged by bad luck — and Winker's dog has a lot to do with it!

UNDER MY UMBRELLA… ELLA… ELLA…

In one of the strangest of all the Dandy's adventure stories, a gang of mysterious criminals dressed as City gents use their jet-powered umbrellas to commit nefarious deeds such as bank robberies and kidnappings. Young Toby Judd is the diminutive hero of this story,…

A battle in mid-air — And one fighter has no wings!

In the nick of time he scooped Toby up in one arm, just as the bull lowered its head to gore the running boy. It stumbled and rammed its face in the dirt, while Toby was borne aloft.

Now the strange bandits headed out over the cliffs. Toby was racking his brain about his next move. He wriggled furiously, striving to get closer to the umbrella.

Suddenly the boy battered his fist against the catch that held it open.

The catch gave way. The fabric was caught by the wind and torn from its struts. Toby was suddenly released as his captor clutched at the umbrella stick with both hands.

Toby glimpsed the figure shooting towards him. He dived beneath the surface, and the clutching hand of the Umbrella Man missed.

Toby was a good swimmer. He turned his fall into a skilful dive. He was battling towards the shore when a bandit came swooping after him while another went to the aid of the crippled gangster.

Keeping under water, Toby swam as fast as he could, heading for the cliffs, which he saw as a dark mass on his left.

By sticking to the cliffside, and only showing his face above the surface to gulp in air, Toby managed to avoid being seen, and at last crawled ashore.

But the rocky cove was ringed by sheer cliffs and the Umbrella Men were circling it trying to spot him. Toby Judd was trapped!

Next week — The navy's here! Can the bluejackets beat off the bowler-hatted bandits?

MECHANICAL MARVEL!

Brassneck, Charley Brand's robotic chum, was invented for him by his uncle, to give him "a friend when he really needed one". Seemingly equipped with every gadget under the sun - James Bond, eat your heart out! - Brassneck got Charley into (and out of) endless sticky situations.

Brassneck faced constant pressure to keep out of certain areas of Charley's life, whether it was at school or in the wider world, but his and Charley's determination not to give in to prejudice makes this a powerful story as well as a funny one.

Swotty escapes from Fatso's ire — But it's out of the frying pan into the fire!

BORDER DISPUTE!

The village of Crosspatch was situated on the Scottish/English border, and had a school on either side: one for the Jocks and one for the Geordies. This was unfortunate, as it led to constant cross-border thumpings and territorial biffings, which caused their teachers no end of grief!

THE PAST ST KIDS!

In this medieval school farce, the kids are so unruly that poor Teacher has to wear a suit of armour... and teachers today think they've got it hard!

The story of a Jack Silver caper— With a plant that gives off knockout vapour!

There was a large ornamental plant outside the glasshouse. Captain Zapp used his stilt-legged machine to kick the plant clean through the armoured glass.

SO YOU THINK YOU CAN KEEP ME OUT, DO YOU?

YEOW!

There was nothing Curly could do now to prevent the Zorgs marching into the glasshouse. He was unconscious.

COME ON, MEN. IF WE GET THE SLEEPO PLANTS WE CAN PUT EVERYONE IN THE CITY TO SLEEP!

GROAN!

Captain Zapp led the Zorgs into the growing chamber. But Jack Silver had been there before them— and he had picked every Sleepo plant in the place.

QUIETLY DOES IT! I MUST GET OUTSIDE WITH THESE WITHOUT BEING SEEN!

Outside, Jack worked quickly, stepping into the hoist that lifted him into the cabin of the first stilt-legged vehicle.

He visited all the vehicles and hid a Sleepo plant in each.

THIS WILL BE A SURPRISE FOR CAPTAIN ZAPP!

By now Curly was on his feet again, and he staggered out in time to see Jack descend from the last vehicle.

Together the boys watched from hiding as the evil Captain and his henchmen stamped out of the glasshouse.

ZAH! NOT A SLEEPO PLANT TO BE FOUND. THE CRAFTY MARSUVIANS MUST HAVE MOVED THEM!

Captain Zapp was about to hoist himself up to his driving cabin, when he noticed something strange happening!

THEY'RE FALLING UNCONSCIOUS FROM THEIR CABINS!

Captain Zapp decided that there must be some sort of booby trap inside each cabin—and he thought of the Sleepo plants.

I'LL MASK MYSELF, BEFORE I GO UP!

Holding his breath, the yellow rogue found the hidden Sleepo plant and hurled it out.

ZAH! I COULDN'T FIND ONE OF THESE WHEN I WANTED ONE—AND NOW, I MUST THROW IT AWAY!

DAN 12.1.80

Captain Zapp's raid misfired completely. With all the Zorg troops lying senseless, the Captain made off at speed.

THE YELLOW RASCAL IS GETTING AWAY!

TOO BAD! BUT WE'LL CORNER HIM ONE DAY!

Back at the glasshouse, the police had now arrived. And they were full of praise for the daring work of Jack and Curly.

GOOD JOB YOU SAVED THOSE SLEEPO PLANTS. THEY COULD BE DEADLY IN THE WRONG HANDS.

HOPE I HAVEN'T KILLED THEM BY PICKING THEM!

NO FEAR OF THAT! THE GUARDS HAVE GOT THEM ALL BACK. WELL DONE!

NEXT WEEK—A scaly animal, huge and strong—With a tongue that's twenty feet long!

11

DESPERATE DAN

Desperate Dan's the "Dandy" glee-man—Next week you'll chuckle at our he-man!

DESPERATE DAN

Next week Danny's tough as nails—To raise the laughs he never fails!

No 1 DEC. 4 1937 EVERY FRIDAY 2ᵈ

THE DANDY COMIC

KORKY THE CAT

Nº1 EXPRESS WHISTLER FREE INSIDE

Keyhole Kate's a little sneak—See her on this page each week.

KEYHOLE KATE

He's the toughest of the tough—Watch our Danny do his stuff.

DESPERATE DAN

Poor old Pussy on the prowl—Meets the Frog, now hear him howl.

YOU, TOO, CAN HAVE FUN WITH THE JUMPING FROG. THERE WILL BE ONE FREE INSIDE EVERY COPY OF "THE DANDY" NEXT WEEK

JIMMY AND HIS GROCKLE

1—Jimmy Johnson got a present in a parcel from his uncle in South America. It was a great big egg—so big that Jimmy thought it was an ostrich egg.

2—There wasn't a hen in the hen-house big enough to sit on it and hatch it out. But Jimmy thought of putting it in the warm oven.

3—He listened at the oven door for a long time. Presently he heard queer sounds like these—"Grockle, grockle, grockle!" The egg was hatching.

4—But it wasn't an ostrich that walked out when he opened the oven. It was the queerest animal you ever saw, right from its funny grin to its funny, spiky tail.

5—Jimmy thought it might be hungry. It was!—for when he put down a basin of potatoes, it gobbled up the potatoes and tried to gobble up the basin as well!

6—What an appetite that animal had! It ate anything, from Pa Johnson's Sunday boots to the cabbages in the garden. And it grew and grew and grew.

7—One day Jimmy tied a string round the queer animal's neck and took it out for a walk. He wanted to show it off to his chums in the street.

8—But round the corner of the wall at the end of the street he met Big Bill Brown, the town bully. Brown was in an ugly mood and started getting tough.

9—Then he spotted the string in Jimmy's hand, and thought Jimmy had a dog with him. So he flattened Jimmy's nose and grabbed the string.

10—Meanwhile Jimmy's queer animal had lingered round the corner to chew up an old tin can. But when Brown heaved on the string, round it came.

11—Wonder of wonders! — Flames streamed from its mouth and set Brown's pants on fire! And Brown ran so hard, his boots must nearly have gone on fire, too!

12—When the strange animal came back Jimmy looked at it. It looked like nothing else on earth, so he called it by the name which it called itself—Grockle.

The funny grin on his funny clock'll—Be here next week; watch for Jimmy's Grockle.

THE TRICKS OF TOMMY

The Boy With 100 Voices

"TOMMY," said Mrs Payne, as she bustled round the breakfast table, "I want you to call in on Mr Crosspatch, the grocer, on your way to school, and ask him to send these groceries. I won't have time to go for them myself, and I must have them for the dinner."

She gave Tommy a list of the groceries she wanted.

"Must I go, Mother?" Tommy grumbled. "You know Mr Crosspatch always growls at me, and I'm late for school as it is."

"Yes, Tommy, you must go," said Mrs Payne. "I must have those things this morning. Run along, now. The clock is ten minutes fast, so you'll be in plenty of time."

"O K, Mums," grinned Tommy. "Cheerio! And cheerio, Christina!" he added to his little sister, who was not yet old enough to go to school.

He went out whistling. But when he reached the street his whistle quickly died away. He never whistled when he was going to the grocer's, and the reason was that he didn't like going to the grocer's.

Old Crosspatch was a mean and nasty customer. Some people even said he was a cheat and a swindler. And he was thoroughly hated by nearly everybody in the town of Crockford. He had got Tommy into trouble more than once, and nowadays Tommy kept away from him as much as he could.

Now Tommy had a strange gift. He could imitate other people's voices. He had been able to do this ever since he was a little toddler. When a person frightened him at that early age, he would answer back in that person's voice.

Gradually he had got over this, and as he got older he had learned to control the trick, until now he could speak with anybody's voice at any time, after hearing it only once. All he had to do was to think hard of the person he wanted to imitate.

Another strange thing about Tommy's imitation of anybody's voice was that it didn't seem to come from Tommy, but just seemed to float out of nowhere.

Tommy looked around to see that there was no one about in the street. Then he thought hard of old Crosspatch.

"Ah, you young varmint!" he growled in Crosspatch's voice. "I'll set the police on your track!"

Tommy rubbed his hands. That was exactly how the grocer spoke, and he knew old Crosspatch would say something like that.

"Old sour face!" thought Tommy as he came in sight of the grocer's shop.

The shop was big and dark, and there were stacks of biscuit tins and sacks of potatoes piled up just inside the door, so that you walked along a sort of alley to get inside the shop.

Tommy had turned into this alley and he was about to step into the shop when he came to a sudden halt. A small boy's cry of pain had rung through the shop, and it was followed by old Crosspatch's angry voice.

"Shut up, you young rascal!" Tommy heard the grocer say. "I don't want any of your snivelling tricks in here. Now what are you going to tell your mother?"

There was no reply—only a sound of sobbing. Tommy peered round a pile of biscuit tins to see what was happening. There was Crosspatch, leaning right over the counter and gripping a little chap a bit younger than Tommy by the collar.

"Well, what are you going to tell your mother?" repeated the grocer, shaking the little chap until his teeth rattled.

"I—I don't know!"

"You do know! You're going to tell her that you and some of your young scoundrels of companions ate those apples which she says were missing from the basket of groceries you took home to her. Now, that's what you're going to tell her, isn't it?"

"N—no!" stammered the boy. "I—I didn't eat them."

"You're going to say you did!"

"But I didn't. You couldn't have put them into my basket."

Tommy's fists clenched as old Crosspatch shook the boy again.

"Listen!" snarled the grocer. "You'll tell your mother you ate those apples, or I'll tell the police you were playing football in the street last night and nearly broke my window!"

A scared look came into the little chap's eyes, and he was silent for a moment. Then he seemed to decide that a whacking from his mother wouldn't be quite as bad as being reported to the police.

"All—all right, Mr Crosspatch," he faltered at last, and when the grocer let him go he scurried away into the street, not even noticing Tommy as he flashed past.

Tommy peered into the shop again. There was the grocer, smiling broadly.

"That was easy money!" Tommy heard him say.

"The dirty twister!" growled Tommy, and he drew back, boiling with rage.

It was quite clear now that Crosspatch was really a cheat, just as some people said. He had taken the money for the apples from the little fellow, but hadn't given him any apples. His mother had received all the other groceries she had ordered, but had sent her son back for the apples. And now Crosspatch had bullied the boy into promising to tell his mother that he had eaten them.

It was a mean, foul trick, such as only the greediest miser would think of playing. Tommy wondered what he should do. If he told the police, the grocer would only laugh at his story.

So he racked his brains desperately. The only thing would be to show up the grocer in his true colours, but how could that be done?

Then Tommy hit on a great idea. He decided he could fix old Crosspatch if he could make him wild enough to come along and complain to Tommy's Headmaster, as Crosspatch usually did when he was wild at boys. The Headmaster was quite a big man in Crockford, and when he saw Crosspatch shown up he would know how to deal with him.

The problem of how the showing up was to be done didn't worry Tommy just then. He just shoved his hands into his pockets and strode into the shop with the idea of making Crosspatch wild!

He advanced to the counter and handed over Mrs Payne's list of groceries.

"My mother wants you to send these things along this morning," he said.

"Ah, you young varmint!" growled Crosspatch, using the exact words Tommy had known he would use. "We've had peace since you started going to school. I suppose you're pestering the teachers like you used to pester me. Go on," he grunted. "Be off with you. I'll send these things along."

Tommy turned away, and at once saw a means of making the grocer jumping mad. On a box near the door Crosspatch had laid a tray of sugar lumps. Tommy coolly stuck his hand out, grabbed a handful, and put them into his pocket.

Sure enough, Crosspatch saw him. The grocer let out a yell.

"I'll teach you, you young rip, you highway robber! I'll have you flogged up at that school of yours, you wretched thief!"

Tommy dived for the door. But he tripped and fell forward, and his outstretched hands went slap into a crate of eggs. He broke about a dozen, and covered his hands and arms with yellow yolk. But he picked himself up quickly, and ran as fast as he could.

Doubling around a few corners, he was soon able to slow down. Crosspatch had given up the chase, and Tommy just had time to get to the school and clean up before the bell rang.

"Well, Crosspatch ought to be wild enough now!" he chuckled.

Shocks for the Teacher

TOMMY was worried. Mr Paxton, his teacher, was giving a history lesson that morning. He was telling the class briefly about the Kings of England, and had got as far as Henry the Eighth. But Tommy was paying no attention to him. His mind was on old Crosspatch, and he was wondering how he was going to show the grocer up in front of the Headmaster.

Just then Mr Paxton, who saw that Tommy was dreaming, fired a question at him.

"Payne!" he rapped. "Describe in a few words the kind of man Henry the Eighth was."

Tommy started from his day-dreaming and blinked. Mr Paxton repeated the question.

Tommy didn't know what to do, but Blossom, who was the biggest fellow in the class and a proper bully, slipped Tommy a note. Tommy opened the note under his desk and began to read its contents aloud.

"Henry the Eighth was called Bluff King Hal because he was good at bluffing his way out of tight corners. He was married six times and he became a great film actor. He was a star in a film that was shown at The Kinema along the road three weeks ago."

The class was doubled up with laughter, and Blossom laughed loudest of all. Mr Paxton was furious. He took his cane and gave the bewildered Tommy four stingers.

"And now, my pretty Blossom that bloometh in the spring," purred Mr Paxton. "You are enjoying yourself. So perhaps you'll tell us the names of Henry's six wives?"

Blossom stood up and cleared his throat. This was Tommy's chance to get revenge on Blossom for the nonsense he had written on that note. He thought hard, very hard of Blossom, and then spoke out with Blossom's voice.

"Sure, I'll tell you. The six dames that Henry fell in love with were Greta Garbo, Myrna Loy, Ginger Rogers, Joan Crawford, Gracie Fields, and—and Nellie Wallace!"

The class was dumb with awe. This was going too far. Blossom would get it in the neck this time. And Blossom did!

Mr Paxton was speechless with rage at first. He choked and spluttered, and just then the bell rang for the morning break. As the other boys trooped out the teacher took the frightened Blossom by the collar.

"Come, Blossom, we'll see what the Headmaster has to say about this outrage!"

"But, sir, it wasn't me. I didn't say anything!" cried Blossom.

"Don't make it worse by lying," said Mr Paxton between his teeth.

It was a very sore Blossom who came back to the class a quarter of an hour later. Tommy grinned. That would teach Blossom not to get other people into trouble!

Mr Crosspatch on the War-Path

BUT Tommy was still puzzling over his problem. How could he show up old Crosspatch?

And his chance arrived before he was ready for it. A boy came in with a message that Dr Blott, the Headmaster, wished to see Thomas Payne in his study immediately.

Tommy left the room nervously. Now for it! He tapped gently on the Headmaster's study door.

"Come in," called the Head.

"That's the villain! That's the blackguard!" shouted Crosspatch, waving his umbrella as Tommy entered the room.

"Really, sir!" interrupted Dr Blott. "Please allow me to handle this affair!"

Crosspatch only scowled.

"Payne," said Dr Blott, turning to Tommy, "I have received a very serious complaint about you. Mr Crosspatch has stated that you stole his goods and destroyed a crate of his eggs. Now, what have you to say for yourself?"

"The breaking of the eggs was an accident, sir. I slipped," began Tommy.

"Take no notice of the little scoundrel!" growled Crosspatch. "He did it on purpose."

The Head looked at Crosspatch very coldly. It was clear to Tommy that he didn't like the old grumbler, and that he hated all these interruptions. Tommy saw a slender chance. If he could cause these two to quarrel, he might manage to make Crosspatch show himself up. So he thought very hard about the Head. Then very clearly he imitated the Head's voice.

"Shut up, you old twister!" he said. Crosspatch snorted furiously.

THIS GREAT

JUMPING FROG

FREE TO EVERY READER NEXT FRIDAY

"Old twister! What do you mean, sir? How dare you call me an old twister?"

The Headmaster looked puzzled.

"I assure you, sir——" he began.

"—that you are a dirty swindler!" continued Tommy in the Head's voice.

"And you, sir, are a pompous old madman. I'll have the law on you for this!" shouted Crosspatch. "I'll report you to the education authorities. I'll have you sacked. No wonder the boys are thieves and wreckers. Their masters are no better!"

Things had gone a bit further than Tommy had meant them to go just yet. Dr Blott lost his temper thoroughly, and he told Crosspatch in very strong language what he thought of him and his continual complaints.

It was all very funny, but it was not what Tommy had meant to happen. He had hoped to imitate Crosspatch's voice and say things about the grocer that would show him up properly. But now they were both shouting so loud that Tommy didn't have the lung power to make his imitation of the grocer's voice heard.

They hurled threats at each other until they were both breathless, and then Crosspatch grabbed his hat and strode out, nearly pulling the door off its hinges. Tommy looked uneasily at the panting Head.

Dr Blott was wild with anger, and he had to have something to vent his anger upon.

"So you are the boy who caused all the trouble?" he roared. "Good! We'll see what we can do to curb your frisky goings-on."

It was a painful ten minutes for Tommy. His plans had gone all wrong, but as he limped away he vowed between clenched teeth that he would have Crosspatch run out of the town yet. This flogging only made him more determined than ever!

Tommy's Revenge

TOMMY got the idea for his plan of revenge from Christina, his little sister.

His father had brought home some sand, very fine, white sand, to do a job in the garden. Christina was playing with it.

"Look, Tommy!" she shouted. "Sugar!"

That gave Tommy the idea. After his tea on Saturday evening, he went along to Crosspatch's shop. The shop was full of people doing their week-end shopping, and Tommy had no trouble in mixing among

them without being seen by Crosspatch.

He mingled with the customers at the counter, and found that Mrs Breen, the wife of an important man in Crockford, was being served by Crosspatch. She was giving her order.

"A pot of marmalade, two pounds of butter—Empire butter—a dozen fresh eggs—mind they are fresh, Mr Crosspatch. And let me see, yes, three pounds of sugar."

This was Tommy's chance. Mr Crosspatch was an old-fashioned grocer, who didn't bother with the new-fangled methods of selling sugar that was all ready made up in bags. He kept loose sugar in a bin at the back of the shop, and weighed it out as he needed it.

Tommy cleared his throat, and thought hard of Mr Crosspatch.

"Oh, Mrs Breen," Crosspatch's voice went floating over the shop, "I really wouldn't advise you to buy my sugar. I always mix some white sand into my sugar, and it wouldn't suit you, I know. You should go along to Moffat's Stores and buy their wrapped sugar. It's so much better value!"

"Really, Mr Crosspatch!" gasped Mrs Breen.

Tommy spoke out again in Crosspatch's voice.

"Oh, shut up, you old hen! You think because your husband is on the Town Council that you are the Queen of Crockford!"

The other women in the shop tittered. Mrs Breen wasn't very well liked. She had become very proud since her husband had been elected to the Town Council.

"I've never been so insulted in all my life. Sand in the sugar, indeed! Old hen, am I? I'll fetch my husband around to you. I'll fetch my husband!" shouted Mrs Breen, and stormed out of the shop.

"What does she mean? Did she say there was sand in the sugar? What is she talking about?" said Mr Crosspatch in amazement.

"You said yourself that you put sand in the sugar," snorted a woman. "It's terrible the way we housewives are treated. I for one am not going to be insulted by a grocer. Good-day, Mr Crosspatch!"

There were mutterings among the other women, and they all trooped out of the shop into the street. The news spread quickly over the town, and soon a crowd of women gathered around the shop, all of them shouting and shaking their fists.

"He puts sand in the sugar! He said so himself!"

The police had to come and clear them away.

There was an awful row in the town over Mr Crosspatch. Mr Breen, the councillor, wrote a very learned letter to the local newspaper. The town chemist sampled Mr Crosspatch's sugar and reported that there was no sand in it. It was good, pure sugar. But the townspeople were very upset over Mr Crosspatch. There were quite a few who had heard him say that there was sand in it.

So Mr Crosspatch decided to sell his shop to Moffat's, who had wanted it for a long time.

On the day when he was leaving Crockford he wrote a letter to the newspaper. He said he was glad to get out of the town, that the children were wild, that the parents couldn't control them, and that the teachers were not fit to teach them.

But nobody worried about that. And Tommy worried least of all. All he felt was gladness, for he knew he had done the people of Crockford a good service by getting rid of the surliest, best-hated man in the town.

Next Friday in " The Dandy"—There will be another great complete story about some more of "The Tricks of Tommy."

OUR GANG

All these boys and girls play in the famous Hal Roach films of "Our Gang," and appear here by courtesy of M-G-M.

| Spot The Pup | Alfalfa Switzer | Scotty Beckett | Darla Hood | Billy Thomas | Porky Lee | Patsy May | Spanky McFarland | Buckwheat Thomas |

1—There was a big meeting in the Gang Clubhouse the other day, with Buckwheat Thomas, Scotty Beckett, Alfalfa Switzer, Billy Thomas, Darla Hood, Spanky McFarland, and Porky Lee all present. Even Spot the Pup was there, and everybody except Alfalfa was trying to think of something the Gang could do. Alfalfa folded his arms and thought of nothing. You see, he sprained his brain when he was learning the A B C, and he hasn't done any thinking since!

2—Then in came Baby Patsy May with a proper brainwave. "Let's make a fire engine," she said. Billy Thomas got so excited at the notion that she hit Alfalfa on the head with the mallet. But nobody noticed this, because it made the same sound as if the mallet had hit the wooden box. Porky was dreaming of food as usual, and his dreams came true, for his hair was ironed out by Scotty's meaty feet.

3—And here's how the Gang got busy with the job of building their fire engine. Just look at Scotty with the old back axle, and Buckwheat Thomas with the garden seat. Buckwheat was mighty worried about that seat. He couldn't help thinking, "Wonder if Pa will get a drop when he sits down in the place where it was and finds it isn't there?" Darla Hood vowed she would take a lesson in snake-charming before handling a fire hose again.

4—But there was no slacking. In two wags of Spot's tail that fire engine began to look real, with wheels, seats, a bell, and even a ladder. Then along came Buckwheat and Spanky McFarland with an old barrel to serve as a water tank. Billy Thomas cheered them on, but they wouldn't have thought so much of her cheers if they had known she was inside the barrel.

5—"What will we do for a motor?" asked Spanky. "Motor nix!" said Buckwheat. "We gotta dog." And Spot was trying to tell everybody that he was only a 1 Dog Power dog when Alfalfa came along with a 10 Horse Power horse. It was a real fireman's horse, too, for it wore a helmet—though it was only a straw helmet. However, they yoked him up and got ready.

6—"I'm firemaster on this job," chortled Spanky. As he was the best fighter in the Gang, no one argued. So off went the latest 1937 fire brigade, and the four-legged engine, galloping along with a horse-laugh on its face, was a great success. It had lost a shoe, and had a bit of a limp until Scotty found that one of his father's boots fitted its hoof!

7—Round the town they dashed, but never a fire did they see. However, they upset Fruity Funnyface's apple cart and Alfalfa did himself a bit of good by catching the fruit as it fell. Buckwheat was greedier. He tried to catch a lot in his hat, but forgot that the hat had no crown! Ninety-year-old Gaffer Smith had to hop out of the way like a nine-year-old, and the engine was two miles away before he got his breath back.

8—Then all of a sudden, as they thundered up towards Buttercup Farm, where they thought they might start a fire of their own, a couple of nasty tramps sprang out and stopped the engine. "Scram outa this!" said one. "We don't want you guys snooping around!" snarled the other, and he presented Alfalfa with a copy of his fingerprints, and Spot the Pup with a sample of his footprints.

9—So the Gang had to turn and go back, and they went with their hearts in their boots. Even the horse's heart must have been down in Scotty's father's boot. "It's funny these brutes turned us out," said Scotty. "They've got no right to the farm. It don't belong to them!" Alfalfa gave a shout. "Gee! You're right. Guess they're up to no good. Maybe they're the two toughs the cops are looking for."

10—Meanwhile the fire engine had drifted back to town, and Scotty and Alfalfa had just wandered off to see if they could smell out a fire when Fatty came tearing up. "Hi, kids!" he yelled. "I got the good news." Yes, sure enough there was a fire up the road. The engine was turned round faster than a merry-go-round. "All aboard," roared Spanky, and off dashed the brigade.

11—Up the road they went like a streak of greasy lightning. And they took the first bend so fast that there was a biff! and a smack! That fire engine had given the two town cops a tip—yes, a tip into the ditch! But the Gang didn't mind. They were getting the hose ready. Alfalfa was jumping up and down as if his pants were full of nettles. He could see smoke ahead.

12—Near Buttercup Farm they found the fire all right. Clouds of smoke came pouring over the hedge. So Firemaster Spanky grabbed the hose while Scotty worked the pump. Porky got the bellows, Billy Thomas used her water pistol, Darla Hood filled her mother's jug, and Baby Patsy May got so tied up in the hose that she splashed enough tears to put a damper on any fire.

13—The water went whoosh! over the hedge. And what do you think the fire was? The two tramps had stolen a chicken and were roasting it for dinner over a fire they had built in the field. The water flattened them out, and they hadn't had a bath for so long that they nearly passed out with the shock. So the Gang jumped on them.

14—Then up came the cops. The Gang thought they were in for trouble, but when the two boys in blue saw the tramps they gave a cheer. "Great work, kids!" they sang out. "Them's the two we want, and there's a fat reward for capturing them." And so the Gang had puffs and pies and pastries galore that night. And who ate most? Why, Porky Lee!

Our Gang has lots of laughs for you—In next week's "Dandy," No. 2.

RED HOOF

Son of a Deer-Stalker

THE wind blew keenly down Glen Gorm as a boy toiled up the slope on the western side.

Sturdy, red-cheeked, sure-footed, Ian Duncan was quite a little fellow, yet already he was perfectly at home in the hills. Whenever he got back from school it was his daily task to take his father's lunch to him, wherever he might be in the vast Gairnshee deer forest.

To-day he knew he would find his father somewhere at the head of the glen, where in a certain hollow a good many deer had come down to feed on the tender new heather shoots.

In his hand he carried a large basket containing sandwiches and a flask of hot tea. Big John Duncan would be glad of the tea, for he was the head deer-stalker on this estate, and had been out since early morn watching the herd.

The basket was heavy, and more than once the boy set it down to rest his arm. Several times he turned to glance back down the glen, where in the distance he could see the roof and the smoking chimney of the croft where he lived. There, he knew, his mother would be preparing the mid-day meal, and his small sister, Bessie, would be playing on the hearthrug. He would be glad when little Bessie grew big enough to come out with him on the hills.

Ian loved the hills, and the heather-scented wind on his face. Already he knew every burn and every crag within three miles of his home in the Highlands. Already he knew the haunts of the deer and their movements throughout the four seasons.

Now he was at the top of the slope on the west side of the glen, walking more easily along the ridge, and straining his eyes for a glimpse of his father. If he had been bigger and stronger he might have shouted, but the wind was so powerful that he knew it would drown his voice. So he had to rely on his eyes to find his father.

Suddenly he quickened his step, turning slightly towards the east. He had seen the deer, more than two hundred of them, sheltering in the far end of the hollow which he had been heading for. There were many young calves feeding with them.

On the hill ridge above the deer he saw his father, big, boldly outlined against the grey sky. John Duncan had already seen his son, and was waving his stick.

Ian smiled gladly. There would be no fear of his father having a late lunch this day. It was not yet twelve o'clock.

He started to run; and before long came up with the broad-shouldered man, who leaned on his stick watching the movements of the herd below. John Duncan was a slow-moving man, with clear, all-seeing eyes, slow to anger and slow to rouse, but a man who could hold his own out there on the hills with either man or beast.

Others said he was the finest stalker in all Ross-shire. Ian quite believed this. To him his father was the finest and cleverest man in the world. There was not a thing he did not know about the wild birds, the deer, the foxes, the mountain cats, and the eagles.

"Hullo, son, you found me quickly to-day!"

"That's because there's no mist," said the boy. "I was thinking, Father, it would be a good idea if you made me a big whistle. Then when it's misty I could blow that, and when you heard it you could shout, and so guide me to wherever you were."

John Duncan smiled broadly. He knew his son badly wanted him to make a whistle, and knew that when Ian had it he would wish for mist every day so that he might go out on the hills and blow it.

"I'll make you one for your next birthday, Ian," he promised. "See that tiny calf down there? I think that's the smallest one I've ever shown you. It's the youngest deer in the herd."

Ian watched the mother deer busily licking her tiny calf. He would have been happy to stop there all the afternoon, watching the deer, and listening to his father, but after half an hour or so John Duncan sent him back home. By that time the basket and the flask were empty, and the stalker was looking pleased with himself and with the world.

"Away with you now, Ian, and don't loiter on the way home. Your mother will have the dinner ready, and she'll worry if you're late. Be a good lad and hurry."

Ian promised, and went off along the hillside as fast as his legs would carry him. He could have gone down into the glen almost at once, but he chose to keep on the ridge, where he could see much further. He even had hopes of glimpsing some of the big stags which he knew would be away on their own, ranging the hills.

The wind was now behind him, but the air was still keen, and he felt hungry enough to eat everything which his mother was sure to have waiting for him. He was eager for his dinner.

Then all at once the boy stopped, and shaded his eyes. He had seen a soaring bird in the sky, a huge bird, which swooped down on outspread wings.

Ian Duncan crouched and became as still as the rocks around him.

"An eagle!" he muttered to himself.

He was very excited. It was not often he saw an eagle flying so low, and this one seemed to be coming lower. It was almost level with the hilltop where he stood, and was diving nearer, coming in towards the steep hillside below the spot where Ian stood.

The great bird passed below the boy's level, and vanished from sight. Ian waited a few moments, then crawled forward to the edge of the steep hill, and peered over.

There was the eagle hovering close to a ledge about twenty feet below, and on that ledge lay something which at first the boy did not recognise.

Then it dawned on him that a deer lay there, still and motionless, quite dead. Whether it had climbed up from below, to stick on the ledge and perish, or whether it had fallen from above, he could not tell, but there it was, attracting the hungry eagle.

Ian watched silently. He had never before seen an eagle feed. He saw it go closer and closer, until at last it alighted on the edge of the narrow ledge.

What was that? Ian forgot all about the eagle, and sat up and stared in amazement. Something had moved behind the dead deer, something which lay close beside it.

It did not take the stalker's son a couple of seconds to realise that there was a calf with that dead mother deer, and that the calf still lived.

Saved From The Eagles

IT was quite a sturdy little deer calf, with a dull red coat, and it stood between its dead mother and the rocks behind, staring wide-eyed at the eagle. The great bird fluttered its wings and drew a little closer.

Ian no longer wanted to see the eagle feed. He felt sure it was going to attack the young deer, and kill it.

So he shouted and clapped his hands. The eagle looked up at him, stiffening in alarm. The deer calf made a whimpering sound, and the boy seized a large stone.

"Get away!" he called, and hurled the stone at the eagle.

The stone bounced on the hillside, but that was enough to frighten the bird. Flapping its powerful wings, it rose skywards. But it did not fly away. Another eagle appeared, and both of them hovered high above the hill.

Ian Duncan bent again to look at the young deer. One day it would be a glorious stag with noble antlers, fleet-footed on the hillside, but that would only be if it lived.

There did not seem to be very much chance of this, unless someone helped the little creature. It had no mother to protect it. Down there it would either die of hunger, or fall from the ledge, or be killed by the eagles.

Ian looked about him doubtfully. He could not go back and ask his father for help. It was too far to go, and the deer calf might fall to its death before he got back.

He peered over the edge of the rock wall,

and carefully lowered his legs. He was going to try and climb down to the ledge.

It was a dangerous climb. More than once he slipped, and only the tough roots of the heather growing out of cracks in the rock prevented him falling. His mother would have been very angry if she had seen him doing that climb, but Ian did not think of her then. He was thinking only of the young stag, whch was still making those whimpering noises.

No ordinary boy of Ian's age could have got down that rock wall, but he had been scrambling about on the hills almost as soon as he could walk. Not many minutes later he arrived on the ledge, breathless, and with his fingers sore, and one of them bleeding.

He did not mind that. The deer calf had drawn away to the end of the ledge to stare at him. He could see its soft eyes on him as it wondered whether he was friend or foe.

"It's all right," he said softly. "I've come to help you. Keep still."

But at that moment a great shadow fell across the ledge. It was the shadow of one of the eagles, which had grown bold enough to swoop lower. Ian snatched up a stout stick and waved it to scare the great bird away.

Ian was afraid the deer calf would jump away from the swooping eagle and go over the edge, but it seemed to have the sense to know that the boy was not going to harm it. It remained quite still until he actually touched it.

He was surprised to find how big it was. From above it had looked quite small, but now that he stood beside it he marvelled at the boldness it showed, and the sturdy way it planted its feet.

He caught hold of it and fondled it. Maybe the deer calf liked the warmth of his hands, for it nuzzled against him. Ian frowned when he got his arms about it and felt how heavy it was.

"How can I get it up the hillside?" he asked himself.

He had to do something. The mother deer was quite dead, and time was getting on. If he did not want to worry his own mother, he must go straight back home at once.

In his pocket he had some stout cord, and when he got this out he made the deer calf lie on its side while he tied its legs together, the two front hoofs to the two hind hoofs. The animal struggled, but once Ian had it down he was strong enough to hold it there. And as he tied the hoofs he noticed that, although three of them were black, there was one that was quite red.

"Don't get frightened, Red Hoof," he whispered. "I'm only doing this so that I can carry you."

It took all his strength to lift the kicking calf, and to get its body across his shoulders, with its bound legs across his chest. But once it was in place he had his hands free, and he knew he could manage the climb.

Ian was hot and weary by the time he got back to the hilltop, but he was very proud of himself. He had rescued the baby stag from certain death. The next thing was to know what to do with it!

He could not turn it loose, for it would only die. He could not give it to another mother deer, for she would know it was not her own calf, and might kill it.

"I'll take it home and look after it," decided the boy, and, after untying the tight cords, he carried the calf in his arms down the hill.

It was very heavy. More than once he stumbled because of the weight of it, but Ian had all the grimness of his father. Once he made up his mind to do a thing, he kept on trying.

He reached the foot of the hill, and the little stag struggled, nearly knocking him over.

"Quietly!" he panted. "I'm going to take you home, where it's dry and warm. Maybe we can get something for you to eat. Be patient!"

Long before he reached the lonely croft in its neat garden at the foot of the glen he was running, and as he ran he was shouting—

"Mother! Bessie! Look what I've found! Come and see what I've found."

Mrs Duncan heard the noise, and came to the gate. She stared in amazement when she saw her son, hot and weary, staggering along and carrying something half as big as himself.

"What in the world have you got there, Ian?" she cried.

He reached the gate, and held his burden out to her.

"Look, Mother, it's a baby deer, a young stag. Its mother is dead, and it had fallen over a cliff. An eagle was going to kill it. I saved its life, Mother. Can't we do something for it? I'm sure it's cold and hungry."

The Story of the King Stag

MRS DUNCAN carried the young deer into the house, and very strange it looked in their neat kitchen, shivering and trembling on the hearthrug in front of the fire, staring about it with wide, frightened eyes, wondering whether to run or stop where it was.

Bessie was just as frightened as the calf. She hid in the corner behind the rocking-chair, and refused to come out and be introduced.

Ian forgot his own hunger and tiredness. He wanted to see the calf eat. He rushed into the garden and pulled handfuls of grass, but it turned its nose away from this.

"It's too young to eat grass, or anything else but milk," declared Mrs Duncan. "We'll heat up some milk and see if it'll take that."

They put some warm milk in a saucer, but it was no use. The animal sniffed, but did not seem to know how to drink.

Then Ian had a brainwave. He went to the cupboard and fetched the old feeding-bottle that Bessie had used when she was a tiny baby.

"It's only a baby stag, Mother, so perhaps it'll use this!" he suggested.

Mrs Duncan did not think so, but she filled the bottle, held the rubber end to the little animal's mouth, and, sure enough, it sucked greedily.

Ian danced with glee. Even Bessie came out from her hiding-place to watch. The baby stag emptied one bottle, and wanted another. It followed Mrs Duncan all round the kitchen as she prepared more milk. She said she had never before seen such a friendly little animal.

"And it's got no mother and no father," said Ian. "Can't we keep it here until it gets big, Mother?"

Mrs Duncan felt the creature's soft nose against her fingers as she held the bottle, and she smiled rather wistfully.

"Who ever heard of keeping a wild stag, even a young one?" she said. "You'll have to ask your father about it."

After this Ian could scarcely wait for his father to come home in the middle of the afternoon.

As soon as it had fed the deer calf wanted to sleep, and they made a comfortable place for it with some rugs and old blankets in front of the fire.

There it slept as though it had no care in all the world, and Ian and young Bessie sat down beside it, as still as could be, to watch its heaving sides.

Almost before they expected him, John Duncan arrived home, weary but full of good humour. He knew there would be a good, hot meal awaiting him, and his day's work on the hills was over. With him he

brought Rob, the big deer-hound, which went everywhere with him, and it was the savage growl of Rob that told him there was a stranger in the house.

Then Ian rushed at him, grabbed his hand, and dragged him to the kitchen.

"Look, Father, a real young stag. I saved its life. Its mother is dead. Please, can we keep it and look after it?"

"Yes, please let us keep it!" piped up Bessie, who was no longer afraid of the stranger from the hills.

The stalker looked down at the red-coated creature, and as he did so it opened its eyes and looked at him. Its eyes were clear and unafraid. John Duncan stooped and lifted it in his arms, while his son poured out the story of how he had saved it.

"A baby stag, it's true, but what a size!" marvelled the stalker. "It can't be many days old, yet look how big it is! It's going to be a monster when it's full grown."

The boy's eyes shone.

"But that won't be for a long time, Father! It won't grow up for ever so long. I want to keep it. I'll look after it, I promise I will."

"Well, maybe you can keep it just now, but not here in the kitchen. We'll empty out the stuff from the old barn, and put some hay in there. But look at the breadth of it, and the set of that head! It's no ordinary young stag this, Ian."

"What do you mean by telling the boy it is no ordinary stag?" asked Mrs Duncan. "Why is it different?"

"Because I know the signs, my dear. I know what I'm talking about. If this ever grows up it will be a monster stag, one of the Monarchs of the Hills, maybe even a giant like the one that killed my grandfather, fifty years ago."

"You mean the King Stag they still talk about in the hills, Father?" cried the excited boy.

"Yes, I never saw it myself, but my father told me it stood nearly ten feet high. For years it lorded over all the other stags, and ruled the hills in these parts. Once every fifty years or so such a one appears, but never in my time has there been a King Stag—unless this is going to be one."

Ian looked at the big calf with pride, not unmixed with fear.

"What happened to the last one, Father?"

"It was my grandfather who shot it when it was old and lame," said the stalker. "He brought it down, and thinking it was dead he turned it over to skin it. Suddenly it leapt up, and with one tearing blow from its hoof it killed him. Then it died. Since then there's never been a stag like it in these parts. You can see its antlers up at Gainshee House."

Ian swallowed hard, then threw his arms about the deer calf and hugged it.

"Red Hoof won't do anything like that. He's a good stag, and he's going to be friends with everyone. Can I really keep him, Father?"

The stalker glanced at his wife, then looked thoughtfully out of the window at the rocky glen and the purple hills, with their tops hiding in drifting clouds of mist.

"Well, you can keep him just as long as he chooses to stay, or just as long as he doesn't make himself a nuisance. But don't set your heart on keeping him too long, Ian. Nobody can keep a stag and make it a pet like a dog. They belong to the hills, and to the hills they always go."

Next Friday in " The Dandy "—The story of how Red Hoof fought his first battle.

LOST ON THE MOUNTAIN OF FEAR

1—Major Bryant turned from the wreck of his round-the-world 'plane and looked at his two children, Peter and Patricia. "It's a serious business!" he said. "The old 'plane's wrecked completely, and we're stranded up here." Along with the Major's man-servant, Handy Clark, the Bryants had been going round the world by aeroplane, but they had crashed on a level stretch of a broad mountain top in the Andes Mountains of South America.

2—The mountain was the queerest one they had ever seen. Its top was like a big island raised several thousand feet above the surrounding country on a great pillar of smooth rock. It was impossible for anyone to climb down. But suddenly Peter had an idea. "What about the parachutes?" he suggested. "Couldn't we jump over this overhanging edge and float to the ground?"

3—It was a great idea. But when the Major examined the parachutes, his face fell. All but one of them had been damaged in the crash. "Well," he decided, "I'll have to parachute down myself and bring back help. I'm leaving the children in your charge, Handy. There are enough stores in the 'plane to last you a few weeks—so, be brave, kids!" And after kissing little Pat and shaking hands with Peter and Handy, the Major dived into space.

4—Down, down he went, dropping like a stone. Then his parachute billowed out, stopping his fall, and he began to float earthwards. Peter and Pat watched until Handy's voice broke in on their thoughts. Handy had been a sailor and he was a first-class handyman. "Well, shipmates," he said cheerily, "let's see if we can rig up a tent out of what's left of the parachutes."

5—But Peter was thinking of something else. "It may be months till Dad reaches a town and gets help," he said. "If he's away all that time we'll soon forget what day it is!" "That's right," chimed in Pat. "Why, we might even forget our own birthdays!" "Well, I know what I'll do," said Peter. "I'll cut a notch in this tree for every day we're stranded here. Then we'll always know the right date."

6—By this time, Handy, in his clever sailor's way, had rigged up a trim-looking tent. And while Peter went to help him, Pat said she would go and draw water from the little stream that ran down from the peak in the centre of their mountain top. Suddenly Peter and Handy heard the girl's frightened voice. "Come here! Come here quick!" she cried.

7—Handy grabbed a thick spar of wood to use as a club, and he and Peter raced to the girl's side, thinking she was in danger. But when they arrived they found Pat examining some queer footprints on the ground. "What made them?" she gasped. Handy examined the footprints. "Why, it must have been a Three-Toed Sloth," he said at last. "Look—there are only three toe-marks."

8—Handy followed the footprints for a short distance, then pointed to the branches of a tall tree. "There he is!" he cried. "Watch him!" Up there, hanging by its toes from a branch, was the Three-Toed Sloth. "That's how he spends most of his life—hanging upside-down!" Handy said. "He's slow on the ground, because his feet weren't made for walking. But he's a fast mover when he's up a tree."

9—"This is better than being at the zoo!" cried Pat. But as they made their way back to the camp, Handy was looking worried. "Sloths are harmless," he said, "but where there's one animal there are bound to be others—and some of them might be dangerous." His eyes lit on a lot of spiny cactus plants growing nearby. "There's an idea!" he cried. "We'll build a fence of thorns right round our camp. That'll keep any prowlers out!"

10—With Peter and Pat to help him, Handy carefully built a thorny fence right round the camp. Then, as darkness fell, they made a blazing camp fire and cooked a meal, using the first of their stores from the 'plane. Afterwards, Handy rose to his feet. "Now then, youngsters," he smiled, "off to bed with you! I'll take the first spell on guard duty." And Peter and Pat, tired out after their thrilling day, were soon fast asleep.

11—But there was no sleep for Handy Clark that night. All night long he sat on guard at the tent door gazing into the darkness, and even to a hardened, experienced wanderer like him it was an anxious night. Beyond the thorn fence he could make out shadowy forms prowling round the camp. Their glaring eyes reflected the firelight, and occasionally their howls rang through the night. "Panthers!" Handy thought, but he couldn't be sure that he was right. He had no gun, but he gripped a stout club and waited for the dawn.

12—At long last the sun rose and chased away the mysterious shadows. "Wake up, there!" Handy roared, and Peter and Pat poked out their sleepy heads and blinked to find that it was a new day. They went at once to their look-out spot on the cliff top. Where was their father by now? Peter saw the look of fear that came into Pat's eyes, and swallowing the lump he had in his throat, he raised a cheer. "Hurrah!" he cried, turning to cut another notch in the lone tree. "This is our second day here. I wonder what will happen?"

What does the future hold in store for the three castaways?   See their next amazing adventure in "The Dandy" next week.

The shining sword of the shining sun
In the hands of a boy—the Fair-Haired One—
Shall bring death to the tyrant, so, Tyrant, beware
Of the sword of the sun and the son who is fair!

OMAR, The Wise Man.

KELMAN, The Fair-Haired Boy.

THE MAGIC SWORD

JASK, The Tyrant King.

The Song of the Sword

JASK, King of Shirak, was in a very happy mood. He had spent most of the day watching his treasurers counting the money which his tax-collectors had gathered in from the long-suffering people of Shirak.

It had given the King hours of joy watching his treasurers at work. And now he had arranged a feast in the palace to celebrate the filling of his coffers.

The scene within the great hall was one of splendour. Jask himself, in wonderful robes, sparkling with jewels, sat at the head of the table. On either side of him were ranged more than a hundred lords and nobles.

They did not all like Jask. Many of them hated him for his cruelty. They thought him the worst tyrant who had ever ruled over Shirak. But they did not dare refuse his invitation to the feast.

There was a great deal of noise and merriment in the vast hall. But suddenly, at the top of the table, there was a crash. The King had dropped the goblet of wine which he had been about to raise to his lips. His face turned pale, and his eyes widened with fear and anger.

"What does that mean?" he roared, and all eyes followed the direction of his shaking finger.

He was pointing at the farthest wall, which, like the other walls, was covered with rich cloth hangings. All the lords and nobles turned their heads and gazed with open mouths.

The biggest of the hangings no longer bore the usual royal designs. There were words on it done in needlework with blood-red threads. The words formed a rhyming verse, and it was quite easy to read that verse:—

" The shining sword of the shining sun
In the hands of a boy—the Fair-Haired One—
Shall bring death to the tyrant, so, Tyrant, beware
Of the sword of the sun and the son who is fair!"

Voices murmured the verse aloud, until Jask, shaking with fury, leapt to his feet and swept everything from the table in front of him. Everyone cowered back in terror as the tyrant bellowed:

"The Chamberlain! Where is the Chamberlain?"

Shasta, the Chamberlain, came forward and threw himself on his knees before the King.

"What traitor dared to hang up that verse?" demanded Jask, in a terrible voice.

"I know not, Highness. It was not there when the feast started. It must be magic."

"Magic? Bah! It is some trick. I'll strike off the head of the villain who did that. What does it mean?"

The King glared around, and every man there lowered his eyes, for they all knew this verse by heart. The words were the words of a mysterious song which everyone in the Kingdom of Shirak was now singing.

Nobody knew who had written the song, nor who had first sung it, but it was on the lips of all those suffering people who were ground down by the cruel Jask.

Children sang it on the mountainside as they looked after their fathers' goats, men muttered it over their work, women sang it softly to themselves in their homes. The words had become deeply stamped in the minds of all the King's subjects.

Yet this was the first time Jask had seen it. He nearly choked with rage as he demanded:

"Where is this sword, and where is this fair-haired boy? Bring them to me!"

The Chamberlain spread out his hands helplessly.

"Highness, that cannot be. In all your kingdom there is no fair-haired boy. We people of Shirak are dark-haired. Therefore the rhyme is meaningless."

A look of relief came over Jask's face, and he sat down and stared at the mess before him.

"Let this rubbish be cleared away!" he commanded. "Bring a clean cloth for the table!"

Dozens of slaves dashed forward to do his bidding. The traitor's rhyme was torn down from the wall and thrown into the fire. Then six men brought forward a huge silk cloth, which they unfolded on the table before the King.

Suddenly everyone gasped. The King stared as though he could not believe his eyes. There, once again, worked into the design on the new cloth, was that haunting verse:

" The shining sword of the shining sun
In the hands of a boy—the Fair-Haired One—
Shall bring death to the tyrant, so, Tyrant, beware
Of the sword of the sun and the son who is fair!"

King Jask bounded upright, snatched out his sword, and struck down the nearest of the servants. The rest fled, screaming, and the nobles hurriedly scattered before their wrathful ruler.

"Send me my soldiers! Send me Khast, the Captain of the Guard!" raged Jask. "I will get to the bottom of this. I will find this fair-haired boy and kill him!"

Khast, the Captain of the Guard, arrived in great haste. The King gave him orders to summon the soldiers. They were to make a house-to-house search through the whole city, and the King was going to march with them and see that they searched properly.

"He shall be found, even if we have to enter every house in my Kingdom of Shirak!" vowed Jask, in a towering rage.

But he was really tortured with fear.

The Hunt for the Traitor Boy

THE news of what had happened at the King's feast spread rapidly through the city, and everyone trembled. Long files of soldiers, with drawn swords, marched through the streets, calling at house after house.

"Open your doors, or we will smash them down!" they shouted. "Bring out your children!"

The shivering children were brought before the King, who looked only at the boys. Some of them he took by the hair, and he tugged at it until they cried. One or two, whose hair looked a shade lighter than that of the other boys, were seized by his order and scrubbed until their heads were sore. King Jask wanted to make sure they were not fair-haired boys who had had their hair dyed.

From house to house, from street to street, went the armed men, and they searched every cellar and every attic. But they found no trace of a fair-haired boy. Everyone in the King's capital was dark-haired.

Still the search went on, and as they came near the outskirts of the town a tattered and dirty beggar came and threw himself on the ground before the King.

"O Highness, I think I know where there is a fair-haired boy!"

Jask's face twisted into a cruel grin.

"Speak, and I will reward you with many pieces of gold!"

The beggar looked round fearfully.

"I may be wrong, Highness, but I have heard that Kashan the Swordsmith has a son whose hair is the colour of ripe straw."

"Kashan the Swordsmith—a maker of swords, eh?" snarled the King, and he looked meaningly at the Captain of the Guard. "Who is this Kashan? Where does he live?"

"We all know Kashan," replied the officer. "Many times have I been to his forge, but never have I seen or heard that he had a son."

"Let us go there now!" commanded the tyrant. "If he has a fair-haired son—he and his son shall die."

The soldiers marched through the outskirts of the town to a clump of trees beside the main highway. There stood a forge, with a cottage beside it, and a sign saying that Kashan made swords of all kinds.

But no smoke came from the forge as the King's men surrounded it. They could not hear the bellows working, nor the clang of the hammer. All was silence.

"He has run away!" said someone.

"Burst open the door and search!" ordered Jask.

So the door was burst open, and the soldiers poured into both the forge and the cottage. They found nobody. Kashan, the maker of swords, was not at home. There were the remains of a meal on the table, and one of the soldiers pointed out that it had been a meal for only one.

"Huh!" scowled the King. "That beggar must have told us a false tale. Let him be flogged instead of rewarded, but when this maker of swords is found he must be brought to me and questioned."

He peered at all the swords hanging around the walls, and carried one or two of them to the doorway to examine them more closely. But in no case did he find a sword that looked in any way unusual. In no case did he find one that might have been called the "Sword of the Sun."

He led the way back to the dusty high-road, and was about to mount his horse when suddenly the horse reared back from something on the ground.

The King and his guards glared. There, written in the thick dust as though by a mighty finger, were the words of the verse:

"The shining sword of the shining sun
In the hands of a boy—the Fair-Haired One—
Shall bring death to the tyrant, so, Tyrant,
*   beware*
Of the sword of the sun and the son who is
*   fair!"*

One bellow of fear the King gave, and he leapt upon his trembling steed, drove in his spurs, and fled from the spot—fled back to his palace, where he locked himself in his highest turret-room.

King Jask's eyes were the eyes of a haunted man!

Kashan's Fair-Haired Son

AND about that same time, some miles back in the hills from the spot where the swordsmith's forge stood, a tall and strong-looking man wearing a leather apron was entering a dark cave hidden behind trees and bushes. It was Kashan, the maker of swords, and as soon as he entered, a boy jumped up joyfully from a rough couch at the back of the cave.

Much more powerfully built than any other boy of his age, dressed in a garment of goat-skin, with bright fair hair the colour of ripe straw, he bounded forward.

"Father!" he cried. "It is good of you to come and see me again to-day. I was very lonely."

The swordsmith placed a huge hand on the boy's shoulder and felt the firm muscles under his fingers. Straight in the eyes he looked his son, and studied him keenly. What he saw was good to look upon. In all Shirak there was not a boy so straight, so strong, and so quick on his feet.

"Kelman, my son, you will not have to remain here much longer. You have been a good boy. All your life you have lived in this cave, away from other boys, and away from the city."

"But why—why, Father?" asked Kelman, the Fair-Haired Boy.

"Because it was the order of Omar, the Wise Man, who was your godfather. It was

he who gave me the oils, the herbs and the ointments which have made you grow so strong and so healthy. It was Omar who ordered that you should hunt down your own food, chasing the deer on the mountainside, and the goats among the crags, until you were as fleet and as sure-footed as they are. It was Omar who told me to train you like this, and now I think he will be pleased with you. I am very proud of you."

The Fair-Haired Boy frowned.

"But why am I different from other boys? Why has Omar wanted me to be so strong?"

"That you will learn soon, and meantime remember that you are happier here than you would be in the great city. All these years I have hidden you here, away from the eyes of men, and perhaps you have believed you have missed many things. That is not so, my son. All you have missed is unhappiness. The people of Shirak are very unhappy under their tyrant King. Here in your cave you are perhaps the happiest in the land. Tell me, lad, have you been wrestling with those trees as I taught you?"

"Yes, Father, and now I can uproot a tree a foot thick," said the boy, proudly.

"That is good." The swordsmith stripped off his apron and his tunic, baring himself to the waist. "We will have a match, lad. It will be my strength against your cunning and speed. Come and see if you can throw me yet."

They faced each other in the cave, circling round with hands held ready. And then, with the speed of light itself, the boy darted in and grasped his father's powerful leg. He gripped with both hands, but the swordsmith promptly fell forward on top of his son, caught him by the waist, lifted him high in the air, and dashed him down with great force.

"You were not quick enough, son," he

panted. But then he broke off with a gasp of sheer amazement.

He had thrown the boy with such force that Kelman should have fallen heavily on his back. But the fall had not come about! The fair-haired youngster had landed on his feet, as lightly as a feather, and darted in a second later.

This time he caught his father by both legs, and heaved. The swordsmith was a mighty man. He stood like an oak tree in the wind, scarcely swaying. But suddenly the boy straightened his supple back, and Kashan the Swordsmith found himself flat on the ground, with his son kneeling on top of him, pinning his brawny shoulders down.

The swordsmith gave a roar.

"Loose me, son, for you have won! You have thrown me! For the first time in thirty years someone has thrown me, and it is my own son who has done it! I am prouder of you than ever."

The boy helped him to his feet, and stood there panting with his efforts, his face flushed with triumph.

"I really won, Father?" he asked. "It was a fair throw? You were trying your hardest?"

"I tried harder than ever before, but there is no wrestler living who could have stood against that second attack of yours, my boy. I am very, very pleased with you."

He slipped his arm about the boy's shoulders, and as they stood like that for a moment, something whistled between their heads, and stuck quivering and humming in a crack in the wall beyond.

Father and son sprang apart, and stared at the weapon which had come hurtling through the cave entrance.

"It's a javelin, Father, and there's a piece of paper tied round the shaft," cried the Fair-Haired Boy.

A strange look came into the swordsmith's face as he reached for the javelin and examined the paper. In bold, plain letters on it was a message:

"Kashan, the time has come. Your son is ready for the tests. You have reared him and trained him as I ordered. Now I must see the result. Bid him come to my secret cave. Let him take the path beside the brook as far as the dark wood, then follow the hooting of the owl until he comes to the big rocks. There I shall await him.—Omar."

The swordsmith had read the strange note aloud, and the boy's eyes widened.

"What does it mean?" he whispered.

"It means, my son, that the time has come when you will learn what the future holds for you. You must go to Omar the Wise Man, following the directions he has given, and you must not be afraid. He will tell you the great task in store for you, and what you are going to do for your country."

The Fair-Haired Boy gazed out through the cave mouth, looked at the clear sky, and the waving trees. So far he had seen very little of the world beyond the woods where he had lived hidden all these years. Now he was anxious to see more of it, and to learn why he had been brought up in this strange way.

"I will go, Father," he said softly. "I will go at once."

Next Friday in "The Dandy"—The Fair-Haired Boy faces the first of his terrible tests.

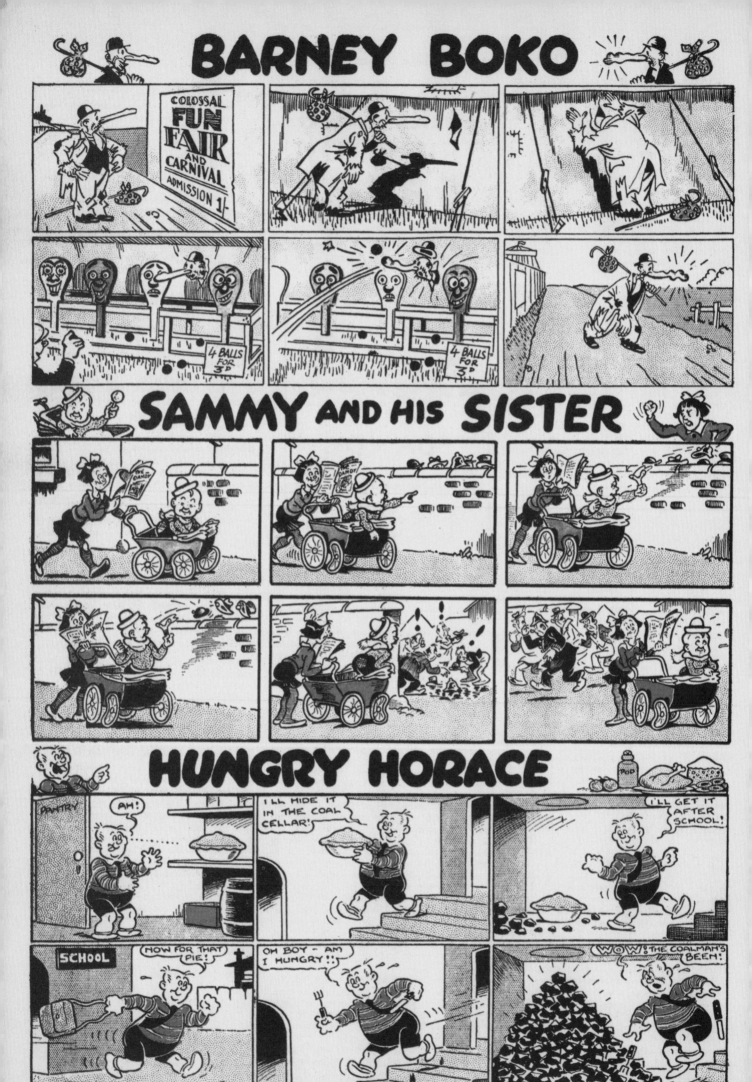

THE DARING DEEDS OF BUCK WILSON

1—Buck Wilson, the stalwart young rider from Texas, came down the prairie trail to Five Forks on Snowfire, his great white horse. Buck was a roving rider who carried all his belongings tied to his saddle. And he didn't have a care in the world. He was strumming on his banjo and singing an old Western song. Snowfire seemed to like that song, for he cocked up his ears and whisked his tail and stepped out briskly.

2—But suddenly Buck heard screams coming from outside a shack in a meadow away ahead. All in one movement he hitched the banjo to his saddle, grabbed the reins, and urged Snowfire on with his knees. At full gallop Buck thundered up to the meadow, and there he found a mother and her young daughter shouting for help. Running away towards the mountains beyond was a grizzly bear, with something dangling from its jaws.

3—Buck galloped right up to the mother and brought Snowfire slithering to a stop. "What is wrong?" he asked. "A grizzly bear attacked us," sobbed the woman, "and it has carried off little Benny. Oh, help us, please!" Buck's mouth tightened grimly. "Look! The bear is running to the mountains," added the girl, pointing to the mountain trail. With a quick word of comfort to the mother, Buck dashed off after the bear.

4—The mountain trail was steep and dangerous, but Snowfire charged up the rocky path at a reckless pace. Swerving round great boulders, he made up on the grizzly until Buck saw the shaggy brute pause on the edge of a cliff not far ahead. "We've cornered him old horse!" he cried—but he spoke too soon. As Snowfire cleared a fallen tree, the bear turned and leaped down to a rocky crag, with the little fellow still dangling from its jaws.

5—Buck peered over the edge of the cliff and saw the grizzly drop on to a wide ledge that ran along the cliff face. There was a big cave on the ledge, and Buck watched with horror as the bear took the helpless boy into that cave. "Must be the bear's den," Buck thought. "Now, if I jump down there the way the bear did, how am I going to get up again?" His heavy riding boots would prevent him climbing. What was he to do?

6—Buck's mind was quickly made up. He led his horse along to a spot right above the bear's cave, uncoiling his strong lariat as he went. Then he tied one end to the saddle and dropped the other end over the cliff. Next he picked up a stout club and took a firm grip on the rope. "Steady, boy!" he said to Snowfire, and the horse braced his forelegs to take the strain as his master lowered himself over the edge of the cliff.

7—He slid down the rope to the mouth of the cave, and there was the bear crouching over the body of the terrified youngster. It would be madness to shoot it, for the little fellow would certainly be crushed by its vast bulk. The only thing to do was to draw it away from its victim, and Buck hit on a way of doing this. He swung himself into the cave and rapped the bear smartly on the nose with his stick.

8—With a great roar of rage and pain the grizzly rose on its hind legs and rushed out of the cave. The rope had swung Buck outwards, and the bear came after him with gleaming fangs and flashing claws. Quick as lightning Buck dropped his stick, drew his right-hand gun, and fired twice, right between those gaping jaws. Crack! Crack! And the thunder of the shots mingled with the wild roar of the grizzly monster.

9—Those shots had been fired from such close range that the bear stopped dead in its tracks. It swayed on the edge of the ledge, and as Buck swung inwards once more it collapsed and plunged forward into space. Its dying roar rang through the cave and echoed from the cliff face. And before the wisps of smoke had stopped drifting from the barrel of Buck's gun, the grizzly had hit the rocks below.

10—Buck dropped on to the ledge and strode over to where the youngster was crouching in the mouth of the cave. He was a brave little chap, for he hadn't cried at all. But there was blood on his lips, and Buck knew he had been biting them to keep himself from crying. "We'll soon have you home now, sonny!" Buck said. "Come on! Let's see you grin!" And the little chap grinned bravely.

11—With the rope tied round his waist and the youngster in his arms, Buck shouted up to Snowfire—"Back, old horse! Back and pull us up!" The intelligent animal knew exactly what he was expected to do. He strained on the rope and backed slowly away from the edge of the cliff. Buck planted his feet against the cliff face. Then as Snowfire went on heaving, Buck went on walking, and so he brought the youngster to the top.

12—Buck swung into the saddle, and they headed back down the rocky trail to the little shack in the meadow. Never was there such thankfulness as when Benny was placed in his mother's arms. Never was there such a happy scene as when Buck sat down with the family to enjoy a great big meal. And never was there such a contented horse as when Snowfire was put in a stable with a huge pile of sweet hay. When Buck rode out on to the prairie trail to continue his wanderings, he was glad he had been able to give aid to the little family.

There will be another thrilling Buck Wilson adventure in " The Dandy " next week.

The Thrilling Jungle Life of a Baby Elephant.

WEE TUSKY

Kang, The Tiger

WEE TUSKY, the baby elephant, was very proud of his strength.

And he wasn't the only one to be so proud. There were quite a number of baby elephants in the great elephant herd that roamed the steaming jungle, and these youngsters of the herd were continually holding contests to prove which of them was the strongest.

They would try to pick up big boulders, to push over trees with their heads, to raise logs bigger than themselves, or to uproot trees with their trunks.

To-day Tusky was practising on his own. He was straining and tugging at a tree which simply refused to be uprooted. He had curled his trunk round the bottom of it, and was straining upwards and backwards with all his might. The tree creaked, and some of the roots tore out of the ground, but the rest held firmly.

Tusky paused and stamped angrily round the tree. It was really much too large for his strength, but he would not admit defeat. He felt that unless he got this tree out by the roots he would never beat any of the other baby elephants in the next strength contest. So he was going to try and try until he succeeded.

Again he took firm hold with his trunk, and threw all his weight into one tremendous pull. Straining back with head, body, and legs, he heaved until he felt his muscles cracking. And at last there was a loud, creaking sound from the tree.

He put all he knew into one last mighty tug, and without the slightest warning the tree toppled over on top of him.

So suddenly did it come that Tusky shot backwards. He had not noticed that behind him was a steep slope, hidden by a fringe of bushes.

Crash! Right through those bushes he went, and down the slope. Vainly did he try to stop himself. The slope was almost a cliff. It was bare and smooth. Rolling over and over he went, and then—thud!—he found himself in the bottom of a gorge, shaken, bruised, and very frightened.

But he did not remain long on the ground. Scrambling upright, he stamped around, shook himself, drew in a deep breath, and blew down his trunk with relief.

" Whooooooooo !"

He was not really hurt, and by uprooting that tree he had proved himself to be stronger than even he had thought. He would go at once and fetch the other baby elephants to see what he had done.

Two minutes later he found that that would

not be so easy. How could he get back up the slope?

There was no way out of the gorge into which he had tumbled. The slope down which he had rolled was very steep, and he knew he could never climb it. The opposite slope was even steeper. And as for the ends of the gorge, they were closed up with huge rocks that not even a full-grown elephant could drag away. Tusky was trapped.

He became very frightened. What if he could not get out?

The thought made him wild with fear, and he rushed at the slope down which he had fallen. By sheer strength he went up almost halfway, and then he slipped.

Down he tumbled again, and got more bruises.

But Tusky was desperate. He tried again and again. He struggled and scrambled, tried to dig in with his short tusks, but it was no good. Hard, smooth rock beat him every time. He alway landed at the bottom again with more bruises.

Panting, the baby elephant gave it up. The only thing he could do was to call for help.

Yet he knew the herd must be quite a distance away now. As usual, Tusky had strayed from the side of Minbu, his mother, and had lingered behind the herd, looking for trees to pull up. And this was the result. Still, he raised his trunk hopefully and bellowed lustily.

" Whoooooooo—whoooooooo—whoooooo !"

The rocks around him echoed his cry strangely, and he was frightened more than ever. It was just as though the rocks were shouting back at him.

Each time he called, Tusky waited a while to listen for an answering call. But there was never any sound except the echoes of his own cry. Again and again he bellowed, but it was useless.

He was a prisoner, lost from the rest of the herd, and if the other elephants moved on to new feeding-grounds, Tusky's plight would become more terrible than ever.

The thought of being shut down there, without food or water, and with night coming on, made Tusky nearly mad with despair.

He filled his lungs with great gulps of fresh air, and then he tried once more, louder than ever before—

" Whoooooo—whoooooooo-ooooooooo !"

Surely some of the elephants would hear his call this time ! His big ears stood out from the side of his head as he strained to listen, and suddenly his heart gave a great thump. He had heard a movement at last. Was it Minbu, his mother, who was coming?

Joyfully he raised his head, and stared at the edge of the gorge right above him.

The bushes parted, and a head appeared. Tusky took one look at it, and then wished the ground would open and swallow him up.

For the head was that of his worst enemy. It was the head of Kang, the tiger, the most terrible beast in the jungle.

With his huge mouth open and his wicked fangs glistening, his whiskers bristling like wire, and his fierce eyes glittering with cruel delight, Kang peered down at the trapped baby elephant.

" Grr-rr-rrrrrrr !" he snarled, and licked his lips in horrible fashion.

Wee Tusky's Hour of Terror

WEE TUSKY knew what Kang was thinking. Kang was telling himself that young elephant was very tender, and that it made a splendid dinner !

Many a time Minbu, the mother of Tusky, had warned him never to go near Kang. Twice Minbu had fought with the striped giant, and twice she had beaten him after a dreadful struggle. But Kang was so strong and so fierce that even Minbu had failed to slay him.

Only old Mawk, the leader of the elephant herd, could have killed the tiger, and Kang was clever enough to keep away from old Mawk. He took care to attack only deer, zebras, baby elephants, and smaller animals— in fact, just the ones he knew he could overpower.

Tusky nearly collapsed with fear when he saw the brute crouching to spring down on him. He knew the force in those mighty paws. He knew the strength of those cruel fangs. Down in the bottom of the narrow gorge there would be no room for him to dodge. He would just have to stand there and be mauled.

He raised his eyes to see what the tiger was doing.

Once, twice, three times Kang leaned over as though to spring, but each time he hung back. And it dawned on Tusky that the tiger was wondering how he would get back out of the gorge again after he had made his kill.

For the first time Tusky was pleased that the sides of the gorge were so steep and so smooth. Kang could spring down on him, but he wouldn't do it unless he was sure he could get back up again.

" Grr-rrrrr-rrrrr !" snarled the tiger, and this time he sounded angry.

He straightened up and looked about him. He was still licking his lips, but for the moment he was baffled.

Tusky breathed again. In the meantime he was safe. But he felt sure that Kang would be clever enough to find some way of getting at him before long.

The baby elephant decided that his one chance was to bring help, so he bellowed again and again.

Crash ! A big rock came hurtling down from above and narrowly missed him. The head of Kang appeared over the edge of the gorge once more. It was the tiger who had pushed the rock over, and Tusky wondered why.

Crash! Crash! More boulders came bouncing down, and Tusky had to move fast to dodge them. He wondered if Kang was trying to bury him alive.

Then all was silent for a time, until he heard something heavy being dragged towards the edge of the gorge. Kang was tugging and straining and grunting as he gripped it with his teeth and heaved it along.

The end of a tree trunk came over the edge. It was slowly moving outwards as the tiger tugged it along by the stump of a broken-off branch.

The baby elephant understood Kang's plot in a flash. Kang had thrown down boulders to form a pile at the foot of the steep slope. Now he was going to topple this long tree trunk over the edge so that it would stand on end on the pile of boulders and reach to the top of the gorge.

Once this was done he would be able to run down it, kill and eat Tusky, and climb up again. His long, sharp claws would easily find a hold in the thick bark.

More and more of the tree trunk came into view. It was beginning to topple over. Tusky watched it with wide eyes, and trembled once more. What could he do now?

Down came the big log, with Kang still clinging to the top end. And then Tusky acted quickly, reaching up with his trunk and gripping the lower end.

The log was very heavy, but Tusky had made his trunk strong by trying to pull trees out of the ground. He staggered under the weight, but managed to push the log upwards.

The tiger could use only his teeth. He growled as he thrust forward.

It was a strange form of tug-o'-war, with the baby elephant trying to push the tree out and the tiger trying to push it into the gorge. It went on for some time, and Tusky began to get tired. He could not keep this up much longer.

Snarling and growling, Kang was using all his great strength, almost falling over the edge of the gorge in his excitement. Tusky panted and swayed from side to side, and then he had a brilliant idea.

When he had been heaving the tree out of the ground at the top of the slope, and it had suddenly given way, he had over-balanced. What would happen if Kang lost his balance in the same way?

It would be a very risky thing to try, but it seemed the only thing Tusky could do.

He timed things nicely. Just as Kang gave an extra hard push, the baby elephant let go and jumped to one side.

Crash! Down came the heavy tree, and down came Kang with it. He turned head over heels as he fell through the air, and then—thud!

He landed on his back with enough force to have killed anything else, but it didn't kill Kang. It only shook him up and drove the breath out of him.

Tusky was shivering with fright, but he knew he had to act again. In another few moments the tiger would be up and at him. The baby elephant rushed in, grabbed one end of the tree trunk, lifted it, and tossed it on top of Kang.

The tiger let out a roar. Tusky had not been able to lift the whole tree, but only one end. Yet even one end of it was heavy enough to pin the tiger to the ground.

But Tusky was not satisfied with that. He did not feel safe until he had stepped up and stood on the tree, adding his ton weight to the weight of the tree.

Roars and screeches of anger and pain came from the maddened tiger. He tore at the tree with teeth and claws, making the splinters fly. But that did not ease the weight on his chest. He was held as though in a vice.

Tusky gradually got back his courage. He even picked up some stones and hurled them at Kang. And that made Kang madder than ever.

Louder and louder rang his cries. The sides of the gorge took up the echoes, and those echoes carried further than the cries of Tusky ever could.

The baby elephant balanced himself firmly. He was going to stand there as long as he could. He knew his doom would be sealed the moment he stepped off.

Minbu to the Rescue

MANY beasts heard the dreadful bellowing of Kang, and wondered what was happening.

Monkeys in the tree-tops and zebras in the grassy clearings, buffalo down by the water and crocodiles in the mud, all heard the uproar. They looked at each other, as if asking what the cries meant. What was happening to Kang? Had the striped terror of the jungle got caught in a trap at last?

Every single animal hoped he had.

The noise was heard at last by the elephants. Old Mawk raised his head and listened. He could tell that there was pain as well as fury behind that outcry, and he grunted with satisfaction. He hated Kang.

The other elephants fidgeted uneasily. The baby elephants were curious, and wanted to go and see what was happening. But their mothers herded them into the centre of the clearing, where all the elephants were feeding.

Minbu, the mother of Tusky, suddenly missed her son, and called for him anxiously.

There was no reply, and she remembered that she had not seen Tusky for a long time. There could be only one reason, she thought. He must have gone to see why Kang was making all that noise.

So Minbu started off at once in the direction of the uproar. Her ears were flapping, and her trunk was curled upwards above her head as she charged through the jungle.

Other beasts who saw her knew that Minbu was very angry, and that there would be trouble for Tusky when his mother found him.

It was easy enough to follow the noise. Minbu came within sight of the gorge, and began to call her missing son—

" Whoooo-whoooo-whoooo !"

But Tusky, down there at the bottom of the gorge, with the tiger making all that uproar close to him, did not hear his mother.

More angry than ever, Minbu went forward. She knew about the gorge, and guessed that Kang had fallen into it. She did not mind about that. In fact, she was rather glad about it. But where was Tusky?

Gradually she worked nearer the edge of the gorge, and it was only by chance that she looked over.

Minbu drew back with a horrified squeal. She had found her son. There was Tusky at the bottom of the gorge, twenty feet below the level of the ground, standing on a tree trunk that rested on the roaring tiger!

Minbu was horrified.

" Whooooooooooo !" she roared, and Tusky gave a glad squeal when he heard her.

He thought he was safe. Surely his mother could help him now! Looking up, he saw her staring down at him, with her trunk dangling over the edge of the gorge.

She wanted him to try and grasp it and be pulled up, but it was far beyond his reach.

Minbu knelt down. She leaned over as far as possible without losing her balance, and that made matters better.

But still Tusky could not reach the end of her trunk with his own. There was nearly ten feet of space between them, even though he was standing on the tree trunk.

" Grrr-rrrrrrr !" roared Kang, making wilder efforts to get free. He did not like the look of Minbu. He knew she was clever.

Minbu was thinking quickly. Her son's life was at stake. She turned away, and a moment later came back with a big rock gripped in her curled trunk.

Down it came whizzing, and landed on top of Kang's outstretched body with great force, knocking the breath out of him again. He lay still, not even snarling. It was only because he was very tough that he did not die.

Tusky knew now what to do. He climbed down from his perch on the tree trunk and quickly piled up the boulders which lay in the bottom of the gorge. He piled them one upon the other against the sloping side of the gorge.

And all the time while he worked he feared that Kang would recover and get loose. That fear made him work very fast, and at last he had made the pile of rocks as high as he possibly could.

Again his mother called to him, and he climbed up to the top of this pile, balanced himself carefully, and reached up with his trunk. Minbu knelt down, and this time she was able to grip the end of her son's trunk.

Tusky hung on for dear life. He weighed a ton, but his mother was tremendously strong. Backing away from the edge of the gorge, she pulled him straight to the top, so that he collapsed on the grass and was safe.

For some minutes he was unable to move. He had received a terrible fright. Down in the bottom of the gorge Kang stirred. He was waking up again and starting to struggle.

Minbu did not want to fight him just then. Kang had been taught a lesson. It was time to go. Night was falling fast.

Nearby was a pool. She dipped in her trunk, sucking up a great deal of water, and squirted it over Tusky. He gasped and stood up. That cold bath had brought him to his senses. He hurried after his mother, trembling at the thought of what he had escaped.

Behind them Kang wriggled and twisted until he managed to get out from under the tree trunk. Then he rushed to the top of the piled boulders and leapt out of the gorge. But he did not go after Tusky. He was too frightened of Minbu.

Sore and bleeding from several wounds, he crept off to his lair to sleep off the effects of his rough handling. He had discovered that even a baby elephant could defend itself when cornered.

By the time he got back to the herd Tusky felt very proud of himself for what he had done. He thought he was quite a hero. He was the only baby elephant in the herd who had ever fought with Kang and won.

But his mother did not seem to be proud of him at all!

She remembered only how he had lingered too far behind the herd, and she led him to a bamboo grove where nice long canes grew.

Tusky began to look sorry for himself. He knew what was coming. It was not as bad being thrashed by his mother as by old Mawk, but it was bad enough, and he knew that when he went to sleep that night he would be almost as sore as Kang.

He told himself that he would look well behind him before trying another test of strength on a tree!

Next Friday in " The Dandy "—Wee Tusky's desperate hunt for water in the dried-up jungle, told in another complete story.

WHEN THE WEST WAS WILD

A Letter From Dad

YOUNG Jack Ryan hitched his pony, Star, to the rack outside the store in the little Western village of Three Springs.

He had ridden the fifteen miles from his home at River Bend in an hour, racing to the village the moment he knew the mail had come in.

There must be a letter from Dad with this mail, surely!

"Good-morning, Jack!" said Old Thompson, the storekeeper, scratching his shining bald head with his thumb-nail. "And how's things out at River Bend? Spring's here at last, and they do say——"

"Is there a letter for us, Mr Thompson?" cut in Jack quickly.

"Letter for you? Let's see!" said the old storekeeper, turning towards the rack behind him. He reached for the letters in the slot marked "R," and went slowly through them, reading each name aloud.

"Rawlins, Robins, Renton, Brent! Brent? How did that get among the 'R's'?" he frowned, and stopped to take the Brent letter and place it in its proper slot.

Impatiently Jack tapped the counter as the storekeeper went back to the pile.

"Reckitt, Reynolds, Robson! That's the lot!" he said, looking over the top of his spectacles. "None for you this mail, Jack! Was you expecting something?"

Jack bit his lip and strove to hide his disappointment.

"We ought to have had a letter from Dad!" he said in a low voice. "From Oregon. Surely he's there by now?"

"Oh, ah! I remember!" said old Thompson. "Your Dad left last autumn with the covered waggon pioneers for the new country, didn't he? Well, don't you worry, Jack. I guess you'll hear from him when the next mail gets in from Oregon to Independence, a month from now."

"A month!" echoed Jack. "And the spring waggon-train leaves in ten days' time! We'd planned to leave by then, Mr Thompson, to join Dad. Are you sure there isn't a letter for us?"

"Quite sure, son!" said the old chap. "Maybe your Dad wrote, but the letter didn't get through. Lots don't, you know! But better luck next time, Jack. I—oh, good-morning, Mrs Brent! Yes! There is a letter for you! Let's see! Brent! Where's the 'B' pile?"

Jack turned sadly away. His disappointment was a bitter one, and he knew that when he reached home it would be shared by Mother and Lucy and young Jimmy, all

of whom were waiting anxiously for news. There were no telephones and no railways in those pioneer days. Letters were carried by pony express riders, who had all sorts of dangers to face when braving those thousands of miles of country where the Redskins ruled and no white man was safe. So it was that six months had gone by since Dad had left in search of a new and richer land, and in all that time there had been no news from him.

Jack climbed into the saddle, and Star turned and moved away. Then old Thompson's voice sounded from the door.

"Hey there, son! Your letter! I found it!"

The boy turned to see the storekeeper waving a crumpled, travel-stained envelope. He was off Star's back in a flash, and ran forward to seize the letter eagerly.

"Reckon my eyesight ain't what it used to be, son!" apologised old Thompson. "It was among the 'B' pile! It's a good job Mrs Brent came in before you'd got out of hearing! The letter's from your Dad, ain't it?"

"Yes! Yes, it's from Dad!" laughed the boy, trembling with relief and pleasure now. "It's from Dad! Good-bye, Mr Thompson, and thanks very much!"

He fairly leapt back into the saddle, and his heels drummed into Star's flanks, urging the pony to race on the homeward trail at top speed.

As he rode, Jack clutched the letter which had travelled two thousand miles over the most dangerous trail in the world. From the far-off new land of Oregon, away on the West Coast of America, this envelope with its precious contents had come.

On into the sunrise it had travelled, until now it had reached the eastern part of America, which was the only part which had so far been really settled by white men.

Half a mile from his home Jack Ryan began to yell. Nearer still, and he was waving the precious envelope excitedly.

His mother, his sister, and his younger brother appeared at the door of the homestead, and came running towards him.

And the sounds of excitement even spread to the next homestead, and a boy a little younger than Jack, and a girl a little older came racing excitedly to hear the news.

Mrs Ryan trembled as she took the letter from her stalwart young son. A tear glistened in her eye as she saw the well-remembered hand-writing. For a long moment she hesitated to break the seal. But young Jimmy and Lucy and Jack shouted for news, and they all went into the house.

The news from Dad was great news. The long letter told how he had arrived in Oregon after many wonderful adventures on the two-thousand-mile-long trail. The journey had taken nearly four months, but Dad said it had been worth it, for he had got a splendid

piece of land, which he was going to turn into a farm.

When Mrs Ryan got to this part of the letter Jack and the others gave a rousing cheer. But it was nothing to the cheer they gave when Mrs Ryan came to the bit everybody had been waiting for.

"The only thing I want to make my happiness complete," Dad had written, "is you and the youngsters. I have made all the necessary arrangements for you to leave on the spring waggon-train, which will be getting ready at the town of Independence just about the time when you receive this. Our old friend, Pat Daly, will be in charge of the train, and he has promised to give you all the help he can.

"You know exactly what to bring with you, and as for the journey, there is little advice I need give you. You will suffer all sorts of hardships, but put all your trust in Pat Daly. He's the finest trail-boss in the West, and the Indians seldom attack any waggon when he is in charge.

"This is all meantime, my dear. Give the youngsters my love, and may God bless you and bring you all safely to me.—Dad."

A tear splashed from Mrs Ryan's eye on to the letter. But the youngsters didn't see it. Already they had joined hands, and were whooping round in sheer delight.

"We're going to Oregon! We're going to Dad! Whoopee! Yippy! Hurray!"

"Wait! Wait a minute!" said Mrs Ryan suddenly. "There's another bit here on the back! Listen! It says, 'Mr and Mrs Arnold arrived safely, but to save time they have asked me to tell you to tell Tom and Amy to come with you and join the train in their own waggon. Tell Jack to help Tom and Amy all he can, and to remember that he'll be the man of your little party.—Dad.'"

The two youngsters, who had come from the neighbouring shack, now joined in the excited capering and gleeful shouting.

Young Jack grabbed an old banjo, which he twanged happily. Together the youngsters roared the chorus, which the Oregon pioneers had already made famous—

"Oh, Susannah! Don't you cry for me!
For I'm heading off to Oregon
With my banjo on my knee!"

"Wait for me! Wait for me! Wait for me!" screamed Pedro, the parrot, picking up the words and screeching them out from his cage in the window. But Brush, the sleek black family cat, merely blinked and yawned.

The Town of Covered Waggons

THE Ryan family had a hundred and fifty miles to go to the town of Independence, and ten days in which to get there before the great string of covered waggons left from there on its long trip to Oregon.

But there was quite a lot to be done before they could leave River Bend.

Waggons had to be overhauled and strengthened. Supplies had to be brought in from the village. Belongings had to be packed and the homestead sold.

Yet everybody worked with such a will that in three days everything was done, and three covered waggons, loaded up to the canvas, were drawn up outside the empty homestead.

Pedro's cage had been hung at the back of the leading waggon, which Mrs Ryan drove, with young Jimmy beside her.

Brush, the cat, wide-eyed and wondering, travelled in his basket in the second waggon, which pretty Amy Arnold drove, with Lucy Ryan as her companion.

Tom Arnold was in charge of the third waggon, and young Jack was in command of the whole party, and directed the start from the back of his pony.

It was barely dawn when Mrs Ryan gazed at the empty, forlorn-looking homestead for the last time.

She felt a certain sadness in leaving River Bend, for she had had years of happiness there. But her husband awaited her in this new land of promise, where happiness and fortune awaited them all.

So she whipped up the horses cheerfully, and started off for Independence with the laughter of the youngsters ringing in her ears.

They reached Independence a full day before the waggon-train was due to leave, and, coming down into the great valley, Jack Ryan and the others saw the most extraordinary scene they had ever witnessed.

The " town " was just a straggling collection of huts built in the very centre of the valley. But all around, the eye could see nothing but the white canvas tops of hundreds of covered waggons.

At the entrance to the valley a rough barricade had been erected, and here Jack was stopped and not allowed to proceed until he had shown his papers. Those papers showed that the Government had allowed Mr Ryan to settle in Oregon, and permitted his family to proceed to join him.

"Right!" snapped an army sergeant, when he had checked the papers and handed them back. "The Ryans and the Arnolds, corporal! Numbers, please!"

A corporal with a huge book turned pages swiftly and shouted a reply.

"Remember that, young 'un!" said the sergeant. "Your three waggons are numbered 102, 103, and 104. That's your position in the waggon-train when it starts! Now, drive across to the camp for inspection by Colonel Holman. After that, report to the trail-boss. Next!"

Jack got his waggons on the move again, and after struggling through the heart of the camp he paraded before the Colonel.

His waggons were inspected and his three months' supply of stores roughly checked. Then he was passed on with instructions to be ready to move off sharp at five o'clock the next morning.

It was a job to find enough space to camp for the night. Every yard of ground in the valley seemed to be occupied, and still more and more pioneers were rumbling in.

But at last Jack squeezed the three waggons into a spot that had been overlooked, and left his pony to go in search of Pat Daly.

"If you can't find us again, Jack," said Mrs Ryan with a smile, "whistle as loudly as you can, and I'll start Pedro screeching!"

From a soldier Jack found out where he would find Pat Daly, and made his way to a wooden shack at the end of the main street of Independence.

He knocked and entered, but at first could not see the man who was one of his father's best friends.

"Hullo, there!" said a voice from a bunk at the far end of the shack. "Who's there?"

"I'm looking for Pat Daly!" said the boy. "Can you tell me where he is, please?"

"Right here, son!" said the voice from the bunk. "Gee! You're Red Ryan's son, aren't you? Gosh! You're redder-haired than your father, I guess! How are you, son?"

"Fine, Pat!" said the boy. "I've come to report to you about leaving to-morrow. We're all ready, and our waggon numbers are——"

"Wait a minute, son!" said Pat. "Who told you to report to me?"

"Why, I was told to report to the trail-boss as soon as the Colonel had inspected our outfit," replied the boy.

"H'm! I don't happen to be the trail-boss this trip, Jack," said Pat quietly. "In fact, I'm not making the trip at all. You see, I was a bit unlucky coming back to Independence last time. I thought I was friendly with all the Indians, yet I got hit by an Indian arrow. Now I can't travel for a month or so. Still, I'm glad you've looked in to cheer up an old prairie rat like me, son! Maybe I can give you a few sound tips."

"I'm sorry you're not going with us, Pat," said Jack slowly. "Dad said you were the best trail-boss that ever rode the Oregon trail. He said you'd promised to help us, too."

"So I did, son! So I did!" agreed the wounded man. "And it's a pity it's too late for you to cancel your trip now and come with me the next time. 'Cos why? 'Cos this is the one trip I ought to make if I never make another! Listen, Jack. Be careful of Dutch Joe! Avoid him as much as you can, and don't ever get him mad at you. Understand?"

"Yes. But who is Dutch Joe?" asked the boy. "I don't know him. I've never heard of him."

"But you will!" said the old tracker. "Dutch Joe Grutz is the trail-boss on this trip. Once you get out of Independence Dutch Joe is in supreme command! His word is the law. And he won't like you one little bit, Jack!"

"But—but I don't understand," frowned the boy. "Why shouldn't he like me? He doesn't even know me!"

"He knows your father, son!" said Pat Daly. "And he's got darn good cause to know him! Dutch Joe was under me in the last trip we made—when your father went. He knows his job all right, but he's a nasty guy. Nobody likes him. And he was so nasty to your father that when we got to Oregon your Dad gave him the hiding of his life—beat him to a frazzle, Jack.

"So the moment he hears your name—look out. He'll know you in a flash, and he'll make things just as bad as he can for you! Watch out for him, son!"

"I'll be careful, Pat," promised the boy. "I'll do my best not to give him any cause to make trouble."

"That's fine," beamed Pat. "Now listen while I give you a few tips."

The Brass Tomahawk

THE tracker drew on his trail knowledge, and gave young Jack valuable hints that were to prove more than useful to him in the days ahead. Finally, he warned the boy about Indians.

"If you're on guard at night-time shoot at anything you may see wandering outside the camp lines," he said. "It may only be a coyote, but, on the other hand, it may be a prowling Redskin. If you do get into trouble with the Redskins, try, if you can, to see a young chief named Double Eagle. He can do much to help you if he knows you're a friend of mine."

He paused to rummage in an old haversack, then handed Jack something he had taken from it. The boy looked at the object curiously, and saw that it was an Indian tomahawk, about half the usual size, and seemingly made of solid brass.

"I want you to hang this on your waggon where everyone can see it, son," he went on. "It's a—a kind of good luck mascot. Don't ever part with it, son. I'll ask for it back when I get to Oregon next time."

"I'll look after it, Pat," promised the boy, admiring the polished brass tomahawk. "And I'll hang it where no one can miss seeing it."

"That's right, Jack," agreed the old tracker. "Just one more tip. You'll hear some queer stories about a man named Death Valley Smith. Take no notice of them. Just remember the name, and if you should ever meet him, well, do exactly as he tells you, without argument, without question. I can't tell you any more than that, son!"

They talked for a little longer, and then shook hands, and said good-bye. Pat Daly was tired, and so was Jack, and he needed all the rest he could get before the great adventure began the next morning.

Very few of the pioneers slept that night. Bursts of song echoed through the camp, and only ceased when the dawn air rang with the call of bugles.

Then there was a rush. Horses had to be harnessed in the flickering light of swinging oil-lamps. Hasty meals had to be snatched, bedding had to be rolled, and pots and pans loaded.

But at last it was done, and the waggons began to roll away according to their numbers.

Young Jack got his three waggons into position. While waiting to move off he hung the shining brass tomahawk over the driving seat of his leading waggon, and stood back to admire it.

Then Dutch Joe came along to make his final inspection.

He was a big, black-browed, heavily-built man, dressed in leather breeches and a Mexican jacket that was ornamented with silver. He wore a broad-brimmed hat, and carried two big revolvers at his hips.

As he rode towards Jack his keen eyes immediately spotted the hanging brass tomahawk. He scowled and demanded the boy's name.

"Ryan, eh?" he said, after Jack replied. "How old are you? Not more than sixteen, I guess! Where's the man in your party?"

"My father is already in Oregon," Jack told him. "I'm in charge, and——"

"Fall out! Draw your waggons out of the train!" snapped Dutch Joe. "You're not going! There's enough for us to do without looking after a parcel of kids!"

Jack went white and started to argue. Dutch Joe roared angrily at him, and raised his whip.

"What's wrong here?" cut in a sharp voice, and the boy turned to see Colonel Holman reining in his horse.

"Three waggons falling out, sir," growled Dutch Joe. "They're overloaded, and not in good condition. I'm not taking them!"

"Show me your papers!" snapped the Colonel, turning to Jack.

The boy obeyed promptly. The Colonel studied them closely and handed them back. Then he turned to Dutch Joe grimly.

"The waggons have been passed by my men, and the papers are all in order," he said. "Let me remind you, Grutz, that you have signed up to take this waggon-train to Oregon as made up by my men. This party goes with the rest. That's all!"

Dutch Joe scowled, but said nothing. But as he rode on to the next waggon it was plain to see that someone was going to suffer—later on, when the train was well away from the eagle eye of the Colonel.

Jack Ryan's fists clenched. He knew he and his whole family were going to have a tough time on the trail to Oregon.

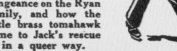

Next Friday in " The Dandy " — Read how Dutch Joe got his vengeance on the Ryan family, and how the little brass tomahawk came to Jack's rescue in a queer way.

INVISIBLE DICK

1—Dick Brett was on his way to meet his pals. "Oh boy, what a day for a game of football !" he cried. And then something amazing happened to him.

2—As he bounced his ball along, he ran into something that felt as solid as a brick wall. "Ouch !" gasped Dick, crashing down in the street.

3—Half-dazed he looked up to see what had knocked him over. And he could see nothing ! Then suddenly he spotted a queer-shaped bottle floating in the air !

4—Dick stared hard and his hair stood on end as he made out a dim figure holding that bottle. He turned to run but a deep voice said, "Hold on there, Dick !"

5—Right before Dick's eyes the dim figure slowly turned solid. "Gosh, it's Peg-Leg Pete ! Where did you come from ?" "Out of the air," said Pete mysteriously.

6—"And here's my secret," he whispered. "One sniff at the queer liquid in this bottle turns anyone invisible ! Now I'm going to give you the bottle !"

7—Peg-Leg Pete told how he had got the bronze bottle from an Egyptian who had found it in an ancient tomb. And now Pete was too old to play pranks with it.

8—Dick stuck the bottle in his pocket until he could get a chance to test it, and he went merrily on his way, heading his ball against the wall.

9—But along came Peeler the Cop, a proper rotter who smacked boys' ears whenever he got the slightest excuse. He spotted Dick and gave a bellow of rage.

10—Dick took to his heels, and Peeler's feet were so big he was left far behind. But when Dick was about to join his pals, along came Peeler and copped them.

11—Peeler cracked their heads together nastily. "It's a blinking shame !" Dick told himself, and then he had a brainwave —what about Peg-Leg Pete's bottle ?

12—Dick took a sniff at the bottle, then held up his hand and watched it. Sure enough his hand slowly faded away. "I'm disappearing !" he gasped. And he did !

13—"Now for Peeler!" Dick chuckled, and he set out to trail the big cop. Peeler halted at the next corner, and Dick began his tricks by shouting cheeky names.

14—Peeler whirled round to see where the voice came from. But Dick was quite invisible—and with his invisible hand he reached into an egg-box outside a shop.

15—It seemed to Peeler that one of those eggs sprouted wings and flew at him. Of course, the invisible Dick had thrown it, and it burst all over Peeler's face.

16—The cop was furious. He couldn't see anyone to lay his hands on, but he could hear a voice still shouting at him. So he chased that voice.

17—Round the next corner Dick was laying a trap. He had a tin of soft soap, and he poured it on the pavement. "Come on! Look slippy!" he shouted.

18—And that's just what Peeler did! He came round the corner like a runaway train, and when he planted his boots in the soap, he came down with a thump.

19—Peeler was wild, so he went on following the mocking voice. At last he lost it. But when he heard laughter behind a tree he thought he had found it again.

20—So he charged round the tree and hit out blindly with his baton. But instead of a boy he bashed the police inspector who was chuckling at a funny paper.

21—"What do you think you're playing at?" roared the inspector, flattening Peeler's nose with a bony fist. Peeler was so amazed that he could only gasp.

22—Then he tried to explain, but when he said he had been chasing a floating voice, the inspector thought he was off his rocker. So Peeler was arrested!

23—About this time Dick became visible again. As the effect of the bronze bottle's fumes wore off, his body began to appear, and soon he was as visible as ever.

24—"Oh, boy, what fun I'll have!" he chuckled. And he was right. Peeler the Cop was in a cell, and he couldn't stop the lads playing football now!

If you were invisible, just what would you do?
You'd do tricks that were tricky, and comic tricks, too.
   In "The Dandy" each week,
   You can all take a peek
At the new tricks young Dicky will bring to show you.

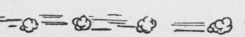